Regional Social
The Central and Sout

Table of Cont....

INTRODUCTORY MATERIALS

Introduction...2
Regional Background Information....3
General Assessment...........................5
Map Skills 7
Map Assessment 10
The Central & Southwest States 11
The Central & Southwest States
Assessment..14
Five Themes of Geography..............15
United States Map............................16

ARIZONA

State Your Facts!...............................17
Things to Do!.....................................18
The Arizona Area! 19
Assessment..23
Travel Time! 24

KANSAS

State Your Facts!...............................25
Things to Do!.....................................26
Come to Kansas! 27
Assessment..32
Travel Time! 33

MONTANA

State Your Facts!...............................35
Things to Do!.....................................36
Meeting Montana!.............................37
Assessment..41
Travel Time! 42

NEBRASKA

State Your Facts!...............................43
Things to Do!.....................................44
Navigate Nebraska! 45
Assessment..49
Travel Time! 50

NEW MEXICO

State Your Facts!...............................51
Things to Do!.....................................52
It's Enchanting in New Mexico!.....53
Assessment..58
Travel Time! 59

NORTH DAKOTA

State Your Facts!...............................61
Things to Do!.....................................62
North, But Central! 63
Assessment..67
Travel Time! 68

OKLAHOMA

State Your Facts!...............................69
Things to Do!.....................................70
It's OK in Oklahoma!........................71
Assessment..76
Travel Time! 77

SOUTH DAKOTA

State Your Facts!...............................79
Things to Do!.....................................80
See South Dakota! 81
Assessment..85
Travel Time! 86

TEXAS

State Your Facts!...............................87
Things to Do!.....................................88
It's Time for Texas! 89
Assessment..94
Travel Time! 95

ANSWER KEY 97

Introduction

Many factors determine who a person will grow to be. The most important factor, usually, is heredity. Other key factors include one's friends and personal experiences, and one's instincts and natural interests. But another influential factor is where that person grows up and lives. A person may endure the chilly winters of the Northeast mountains or the blazing summers of the desert Southwest. Those places certainly impact the person's life and outlook.

We do not, however, live in regional isolation. The modern world has woven a web of interdependency. Each region gives to and takes from the other regions and, indeed, the world. We gain a better sense of where we are today through a knowledge of geography. By giving students geographical information and allowing them to use their own experiences, we can help them to connect the familiar in their lives with the unfamiliar. They can then move more easily from the known features of locale and region to the more unknown quantities of nation and world. Students can begin with the area they know and then expand their knowledge base. Such knowledge will help students in their standardized testing and in their broader academic pursuits.

By showing students their unique qualities because of region and their necessary interaction with other places, we can give them a better perspective of the world in which they live. That broadened perspective is the goal of *Regional Social Studies.*

Organization

This book is broken into three general sections. A regional relations section for the teacher provides basic information about how the states in the region are related. An introductory section for students provides basic material on map skills, the five themes of geography, and a general background of the region under study. The states section for students then gives background information on each individual state. Topics include history, landscape, natural resources, climate, economy, and famous people. A travel guide is included for each state, with details on popular places to visit and activities for students to complete. Each state unit includes map or globe activities, as well as activities on the history, culture, and geography of the state.

Assessment

A variety of assessments is included in *Regional Social Studies.* At the beginning of the book is a general assessment about the region, states in the region, and basic map skills. Assessments are also included in the introductory section for students. Finally, each state unit includes an assessment covering details about that state.

Five Themes of Geography

Regional Social Studies makes use of the five themes of geography: location, place, movement, human/environmental interaction, and regional similarities. Activities are modeled on these themes. Page 15 includes more details on these themes.

Use

This book is meant to supplement the social studies curriculum in the classroom. Map skills help students to improve their sense of location, place, and movement. The regional and state background information serves as reference material for student reports. The travel section helps students to plan real or imaginary trips in their state or region. The low readability level of the information makes it accessible to a wider range of students.

Maps and Globes

Students gain a greater sense of place by knowing their relationship to other places. For this reason, maps and globes are important tools. This book includes several activities that require the use of flat maps, globes, and road maps. Maps of the United States and the world are a handy addition to any classroom.

The purpose of *Regional Social Studies* is two-fold: to give students knowledge of geography and map skills; and to broaden their perspective by showing them the interdependencies that exist among states, regions, and the world. It is truly hard for a person to be totally isolated from the modern world. In today's world of advanced technology and global economy, one must understand and develop links between people of different regions of the United States. One can best show these links between states and regions by emphasizing the five themes of geography.

Location

The states of the Central and Southwest region share a common location. The region is roughly located between 26° N to 47° N and 94° W to 116° W. These states can be found in the west-central portion of the United States. The states experience a wide range of climate and temperature. The Gulf of Mexico serves as a moderating body, allowing the states near it, such as Texas and Oklahoma, to enjoy a milder climate than the flat, inland states. The states of Texas, Oklahoma, and Kansas are also in "Tornado Alley," the midwestern states that experience an increased amount of turbulent weather.

The climate, for the most part, is good for farming. Wheat is a very popular crop; Kansas leads the nation in wheat production. Corn is a major crop in Nebraska. Cotton is a common crop in Texas, Oklahoma, and into New Mexico. Fruit is a popular crop in the Rio Grande Valley of Texas, and also in New Mexico and Arizona. The wide, open spaces of Montana, Texas, and Oklahoma make ranching a profitable venture in those states.

Similarity of location also means some similarity of natural resources. Water is an important resource in this region. This is because most of the states in the region have a shortage of water. Many of the states in the region are part of the Great Plains. The land of the Great Plains is dry. Only short grasses and wheat grow well there. The dry conditions often make ranching more profitable than farming. New Mexico, Arizona, and the western parts of Texas are arid. There is much desert through these states, so water is in short supply and most

kinds of farming are not practical. Major rivers do run through the region. The Missouri River crosses Montana, South Dakota, and North Dakota. It serves as part of the eastern border of Kansas. The Colorado River runs through Arizona. Hoover Dam on the Arizona-Nevada border is a major source of hydroelectric power. The Colorado River also flows through the majestic Grand Canyon in northern Arizona. The Rio Grande runs through New Mexico and serves as the southern border of Texas. Texas also has a variety of rivers, with the other Colorado River supplying hydroelectric power. Oklahoma and Texas have the Red River as a border. Other important resources include large deposits of oil and natural gas in most of the southern states in the region.

The region is fairly large. Much of the region is dominated by plains. The Great Plains extend from the northern states in the region through the panhandle of Texas. These plains are mostly level and treeless, though there are occasional hills and buttes, such as the sand hills of Nebraska. Texas is somewhat of a transition state between the terrain of the Central states and the Southwestern states, and also between the Southeastern states and the Western states. Texas has the piney woods and coastal plains characteristic of the Southeast, the rolling hills characteristic of the Central Plains, the High Plains typical of the Great Plains, and the semi-arid and arid conditions common in the desert Southwest. West Texas also has mountains, as do New Mexico, Arizona, and the western part of Montana.

Place

The common location of the region also influences the region's sense of place. The region has long played a major role in American history. From its early exploration by Europeans to its pivotal roles in the Westward Movement and the Civil War, this region has a common role in the development of the American nation.

Several of these states were important in the Westward Movement. Many settlers made part of their westward journey through these states as they crossed the Great Plains. At first, Kansas was called the "Great American Desert" by explorer Zebulon Pike. As a result, the area now known as Kansas and Oklahoma was reserved as Indian Territory. It was a place the government could move the American Indian groups that proved a hindrance to the expansion of white settlement. In time, though, even Kansas and Oklahoma proved desirable for white settlement. In 1889, the Oklahoma Land Rush set more restraints on the size of the Indian reservations. White settlers rushed in to claim land not set aside for the various Indian groups.

Only one of the nine states was part of the Confederacy in the Civil War—Texas. The other eight states chose to remain in the Union or were not yet states at the time of the war. Kansas, though, saw some of the most violent clashes over slavery both before and during the war. Supporters and opponents of slavery fought often in Kansas before the war, with over 200 people killed there from 1854 to 1861. During the war, a regenade Confederate officer named William Quantrill led his soldiers against Lawrence, Kansas. The town was burned, and over 150 people were killed, most of them civilians. After the war, several of the states had outlaws, such as Billy the Kid. New Mexico, South Dakota, Kansas, and Arizona were known as rough places. Kansas had the so-called "cow towns" of Wichita, Abilene, and Dodge City. These were the towns at the end of the great cattle drives from Texas. Legendary gunfighters such as Wyatt Earp, Bat Masterson, and Wild Bill Hickok served as sheriffs in these places.

Just as the debate over slavery shaped the region prior to the Civil War, racial problems and the struggle for civil rights have shaped parts of the region. One of the crucial trials of the 20th century grew out of a problem in Topeka, Kansas. The trial of an African-American girl, Linda Brown, who wanted to attend a white school, was a watershed event in the civil rights movement. *Brown vs. Board of Education of Topeka, Kansas,* changed the American education system.

Movement

Most of the movement through this region was done overland. Pioneers in covered wagons made their treks across the Great Plains. Gradually the railroads made their way westward. The great cattle drives of the 1880s were prompted by the arrival of railroads in Kansas. Ranchers in Texas moved their cattle to the train depots in the Kansas cow towns for shipment to the East. By the 1890s, the trains had reached Texas, and the cattle drives ended. Texas holds a unique position among the states in this region. It has considerable coastline on the Gulf of Mexico, so that places such as Galveston and Corpus Christi serve as ports. Houston, too, is a major port, but that feat was accomplished only through construction of the 50-mile Houston Ship Channel that connects the city to the gulf.

Human/Environmental Interaction

Pollution is a problem for most states. Humans produce unnatural wastes that are not easily disposed of. This problem is particularly true in Texas, with its many oil refineries and chemical plants. Development has also caused an increase in air and water pollution. Though development and growth provide opportunity, they also cause many problems. Now people in this region are grappling with those problems, just as people in the other regions have been forced to do.

People in this region earn a living in a variety of ways. Farming is still an important industry in some states. Ranching is another profitable occupation. Many people work in the oil or natural gas industries. Logging, mining, and fishing provide jobs in some areas. Many factories in the region send goods across the country and around the world. Shipping and transportation are major parts of the economy, especially in Texas. Texas and New Mexico also enjoy many jobs in the high-tech field. As in other regions, most people in the region have service jobs. They work in office jobs, in finance and real estate, and in the legal and medical fields. Service people also work in stores, restaurants, and hospitals. They also help the many tourists that visit the region.

Region

All these regional links provide people in the Central and Southwest region with a sense of identity. This sense of identity allows students to understand better just who they are. Then they will be able to understand others better, too.

Assessment: Central & Southwest States

Circle the letter of the correct answer.

1. The capital of Arizona is _____.
   a. Grand Canyon
   b. Phoenix
   c. Mesa
   d. Yuma

2. Fights over slavery earned Kansas the name _____.
   a. Fight City
   b. Breadbasket of the World
   c. Bleeding Kansas
   d. the Wild West

3. Many people who moved to Kansas to claim land were called _____.
   a. homesteaders
   b. Sooners
   c. Quantrill's Raiders
   d. Confederates

4. The United States bought the land rights of present-day Montana in the deal known as the _____.
   a. Montana Claim
   b. Gadsden Purchase
   c. Western Movement
   d. Louisiana Purchase

5. The _____ followed the Platte River east to west across Nebraska.
   a. Missouri River
   b. Chisholm Trail
   c. Santa Fe Trail
   d. Oregon Trail

6. The Seven Cities of Cíbola in New Mexico were supposed to be made of _____.
   a. mud
   b. silver
   c. wood
   d. gold

7. North Dakota is in the center of the _____.
   a. United States
   b. Southwest states
   c. North American continent
   d. world

8. In 1889, many settlers hurried to claim land in the _____.
   a. Oklahoma Land Rush
   b. California Gold Rush
   c. Louisiana Purchase
   d. Dust Bowl

Assessment: Central & Southwest States, p. 2

9. A drought in the 1930s caused Oklahoma to become part of the _____.
   a. Super Bowl
   b. Indian Territory
   c. Dust Bowl
   d. Great Depression

10. The most important mineral South Dakota mines is _____.
    a. gold
    b. sand
    c. oil
    d. hay

11. Many American settlers were led into Texas by _____.
    a. Daniel Boone
    b. Stephen Austin
    c. Sam Houston
    d. William Travis

Use the map to answer the following questions.

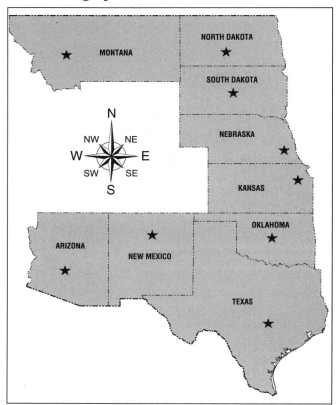

12. The state directly west of North Dakota is _____.

13. The most southern state in this region is _____.

14. The state directly north of Oklahoma is _____.

15. The state directly south of South Dakota is _____.

Map Skills

A map is a drawing of a real place. All maps have a title to tell what the map shows. Symbols on the map stand for real things. To know what the symbols stand for, you will need to read the map key, or legend. Most maps also have a compass rose. The compass rose helps you find directions. It tells which direction is north (N), east (E), south (S), or west (W). These directions are called *cardinal directions*.

United States Map

Answer the questions.

1. What is the title of the map? _____

2. What does the compass rose tell you? _____

3. What does the star symbol in the legend mean? _____

4. Which state is directly east of Indiana?

_____

5. Which country borders the United States to the south? _____

6. Which state touches land only on its northern border? _____

Map Skills, p. 2

Reading a Road Map

There are many kinds of maps. People are most familiar with road maps. These maps show roads, distances, rest areas, parks, and places of interest.

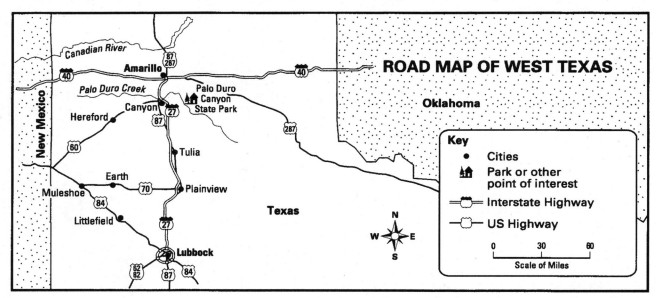

Answer the questions.

1. Find Amarillo on the map. What is the major east-west road that passes through Amarillo?

   _____

2. Find Lubbock on the map. What is the distance between Amarillo and Lubbock?

   _____

3. Find Muleshoe on the map. What direction(s) would you travel from Amarillo to Muleshoe?

   _____

4. What is the name of the park near Amarillo?

   _____

Name _____   Date _____

Map Skills, p. 3

Reading a Resource Map

Some maps show only one kind of information. A *population* map shows how many people live in different areas. A *precipitation* map shows how much rain or rain and snow an area gets each year. The map below is a *resource* map. This map shows where different kinds of trees and forests grow in the United States.

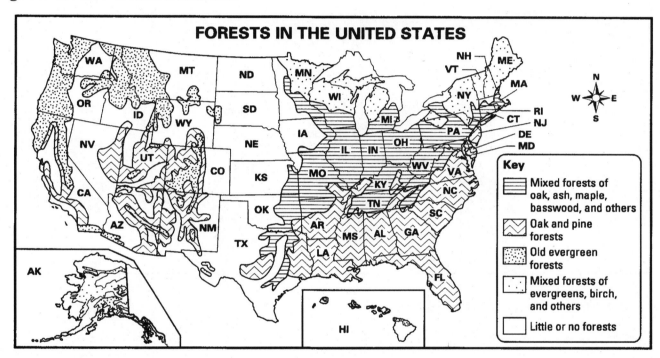

FORESTS IN THE UNITED STATES

Key
- Mixed forests of oak, ash, maple, basswood, and others
- Oak and pine forests
- Old evergreen forests
- Mixed forests of evergreens, birch, and others
- Little or no forests

Answer the questions.

1. In which state would you find old evergreen forests?

   _____

2. What kind of forest grows in the Northwest part of the United States?

   _____

3. How many kinds of trees or forests are in Colorado? Name them.

   _____

4. Find the state where you live. What kinds of trees or forests grow in your state?

   _____

Map Assessment

Look at the map. Then answer the questions.

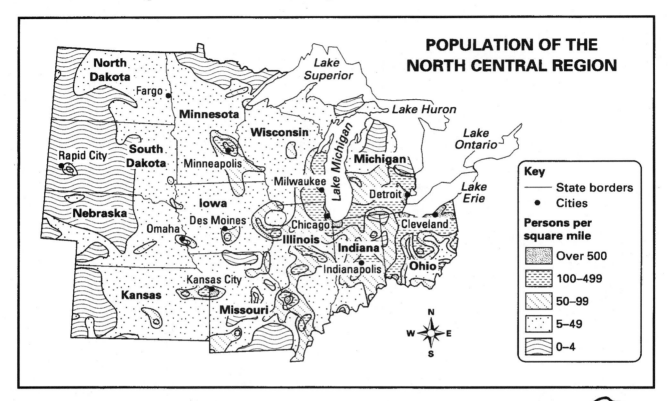

POPULATION OF THE NORTH CENTRAL REGION

1. What is the name of this map?

   _____

2. What symbol is used to show cities?

   _____

3. Which state is directly south of Minnesota?

   _____

4. About how many people per square mile live in Fargo, North Dakota?

   _____

The Central and Southwest States

The states that make up the Central and Southwest region of the United States were once called the "Great American Desert" by early pioneers. The land was mostly flat. The summer was very hot, and the winter was very cold. The people thought there was no use for the land. They traveled across it quickly on their way to the gold mines and forest-covered hills in the West. They did not realize how rich the land was!

History

The Native Americans were the first people to live in the region. Some lived near the rivers. They raised crops of corn, squash, and beans. The other natives followed the buffalo. They traveled from place to place and lived in teepees that could be easily moved.

The French claimed most of the Central states. They claimed all the land that the Mississippi River and its many branches flowed through. This included most of the land from the banks of the Mississippi River to the Rocky Mountains. The French called the region *Louisiana* in honor of their king, Louis XIV. The Spanish claimed most of the Southwest. They had traveled up from Mexico looking for gold.

The United States bought the Central region from France in 1803. The land deal was called the Louisiana Purchase. Texas joined as a state in 1845. The nation gained the Southwest region from Mexico in 1848 in the Mexican War.

The Central and Southwest states were slow to settle. There were no trees to build with. Rivers did not flow throughout the land. To help settle the land, the United States government offered settlers 160 acres of land. The people had to live on the land and farm it for five years. The offer was known as the Homestead Act. The government had also given much land to companies to build railroads from the East to the West. The companies wanted to keep the train tracks safe. They invited people from other countries to live in towns they built. Many of these people were farmers. Mining became another way to get settlers into the area.

With the growth of towns, farms, and ranches, the Native Americans were moved off their land. They were forced to live on reservations. Reservations were pieces of land that settlers did not want because the region was dry and not good for farming. The Native Americans attacked wagon trains and farms. The final battle came at Wounded Knee in South Dakota. Many Native American men, women, and children were killed. After this event, most tribes moved to the reservations with little fighting.

The weather has played an important part in the lives of many people. Drought has hit the states in many years. Floods have also affected the land. Finally, tornadoes have stripped farms. Each time, the spirit of the pioneers is seen. People rebuild and keep going.

Landscape

The land varies greatly in the Central and Southwest states. There is everything from mountains, to canyons, to grassy plains, to deserts. The mountains are young. Some were made by volcanoes, others by movement of land inside the Earth. There are deep canyons formed by rivers. The largest is the Grand Canyon in Arizona. Some states have sandy and rocky areas. Others have flat grassy plains. On these plains, a mesa may rise up. A mesa is a mountain with steep sides and a flat top. These plains were often formed by glaciers. Glaciers are large sheets of ice. As they moved across the land, they flattened some areas. In other places, they left behind gravel or rich soil.

Climate

Climate varies in these states. The Southwest states have a temperate climate. The weather is affected by the winds blowing off the Gulf of Mexico. Summers are hot, but winters are mild. The Central states have a continental climate. Winters are very cold. Cold winds from Canada blast across the land, bringing snow and freezing temperatures. Summers are very hot. Rainfall is limited. The land is flat. There are no bodies of water or mountains to slow the changes in weather. The flat land also causes a big problem in the spring— tornadoes. This part of the United States is known as "Tornado Alley." A tornado is a windstorm that looks like a funnel. The bottom of the funnel spins across the ground. It can destroy whole towns.

Natural Resources

The earliest visitors called the Central and Southwest areas the "Great American Desert." They did not realize the richness of the land. Gold, copper, and petroleum are important minerals. The soil in the

The Central and Southwest States, p. 3

Central states is also an important resource. Glaciers left behind dirt that was good for growing crops.

Economy

People in these regions earn a living in many ways. Most people work in service jobs. These people help other people. They may work in banks, insurance offices, or places that help tourists. Mining is still an important job. Raising cattle and sheep is also a source of income for many people. The Central states are known as the "Breadbasket of America." Farmers there grow most of the corn and wheat used in the world.

Higher Education

Education has always been important to pioneers. They wanted their children to do well in the world. Some settlements started schools in someone's home. Eventually these schools became universities. Some well-known schools include the University of Texas and the University of Arizona. The Sinte Gleska College was the first Native American college in the nation. It started because the Sioux in South Dakota were concerned that their children did not know the language and culture of their tribe. Today, it teaches classes in science, mathematics, and technology.

The Central and Southwest States Today

The states in this region were built on dreams and on hard work. Many settlers started with nothing. Farmers and ranchers faced problems with cold, heat, and lack of rain. In the case of the Native Americans, tribes were forced off the land and into places they did not choose. Their lives were destroyed. As the states move into the new century, there are several problems they will need to deal with. First is the recognition of Native American traditions and stories. Second, many states have a very short supply of water. The lack of rivers and rain means that the states will need to find ways to provide water. Finally, the beauty of the land is very valuable. As people and businesses move to the region, pollution and trash may become a problem. History proves that the people in the Central and Southwest states are ready for the challenge.

Assessment

Circle the letter of the correct answer.

1. Early pioneers called the Central and Southwest states the "_____."
   a. Louisiana Purchase
   b. Breadbasket of America
   c. Great American Desert
   d. Southwest Territory

2. The French claimed the land that _____.
   a. bordered the Atlantic Ocean
   b. bordered Canada
   c. the Native Americans lived on
   d. the Mississippi River and its branches flowed through

3. The _____ gave people 160 acres if they lived on the land and farmed it for five years.
   a. Wild West Law
   b. Louisiana Purchase
   c. Golden Rule
   d. The Homestead Act

4. A continental climate means _____.
   a. temperatures are the same all year long
   b. summers are hot, and winters are cold
   c. summers are cool, and winters are warm
   d. summers are dry, and winters are rainy

5. In the spring, a _____ can travel across the flat land, destroying whole towns.
   a. tornado
   b. glacier
   c. hailstorm
   d. buffalo

6. Reservations are _____.
   a. large farms
   b. the Native Americans' hunting land
   c. places where Native Americans were forced to live
   d. cattle ranches

7. The Grand Canyon in Arizona was made by a _____.
   a. flood
   b. mining company
   c. volcano
   d. river

8. Most people in the Central and Southwest states work in _____.
   a. mining
   b. farming
   c. service jobs
   d. ranching

9. A problem facing the Central and Southwest states is _____.
   a. overcrowding in the cities
   b. recognizing Native American traditions
   c. flooding of rivers
   d. loss of farming land

The Five Themes of Geography

Where people live affects every part of their life, from the foods they eat to the jobs they can do. The Five Themes of Geography help us to look at the importance of a place in our lives.

LOCATION Where is it?

Location tells exactly where a place is located. It can include latitude and longitude, cardinal directions, or even just the words "next to."

PLACE What does it look like?

Place is the part of an area you see. It includes landforms, rivers, or buildings in a city.

MOVEMENT How do people, goods, and ideas move from one place to another?

Movement looks at how and why things move. It looks at why people leave a country, how goods are moved, and how both affect the land or people.

INTERACTION How do people use or change the land?

Interaction is how people use or change the environment, the area in which they live. It looks at where people have parks, build cities, or farm.

REGION How are different places in an area alike?

Region looks at the way an area is divided. A region has characteristics that are the same. Often areas are grouped because the people share a language, people do the same kind of work, or the landforms are the same.

United States Map

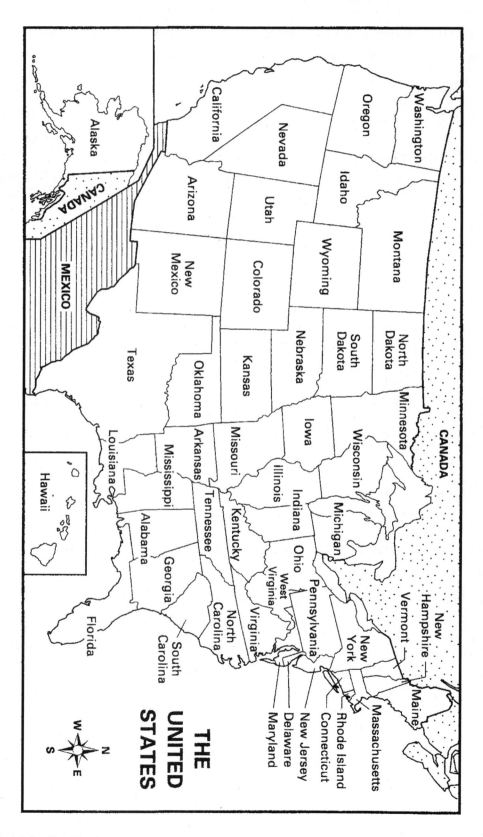

THE UNITED STATES

State Your Facts!

Capital: Phoenix

Abbreviation: AZ

Statehood: February 14, 1912—
the 48th state

Motto: *Ditat Deus* ("God Enriches")

Bird: Cactus wren

Flower: Saguaro cactus blossom

Tree: Paloverde

Area: 114,007 sq mi
(295,276 sq km)—6th in size

Five largest cities: Phoenix,
Tucson, Mesa, Tempe, Glendale

Highest point: Humphreys Peak—12,643 ft
(3,855 m)

Sports teams: Arizona Cardinals (football), Arizona
Diamondbacks (baseball), Phoenix Suns (basketball),
Phoenix Coyotes (hockey)

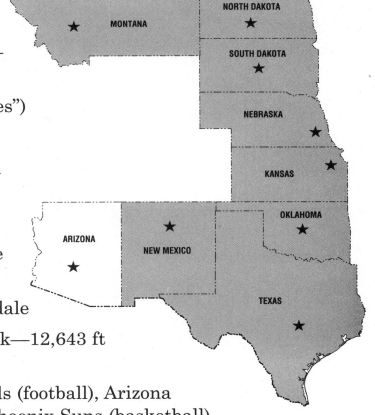

Name _____ Date _____

Things To Do!

Study the map. Then answer the questions.

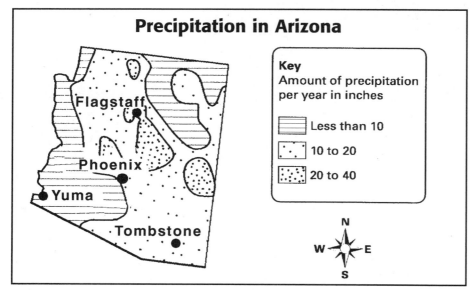

Precipitation in Arizona

Flagstaff

Phoenix

Yuma

Tombstone

Key
Amount of precipitation per year in inches

Less than 10

10 to 20

20 to 40

N
W   E
S

1. About how much precipitation does Phoenix receive each year?

   _____

2. Which city receives less than 10 inches per year?

   _____

3. Of the cities shown on the map, which receives the most precipitation each year?

   _____

4. Which town might be in a desert? Explain.

   _____

   _____

   _____

The Arizona Area!

Before 1950, few people lived in Arizona. The land was mostly desert. However, with the invention of air-conditioning, more people moved to the state. Soon it was cool to live in Arizona.

History

Native Americans have lived in the deserts of Arizona for many years. The Hohokam were an ancient tribe. They dug ditches from rivers to their fields. Some ditches were 150 miles long. They grew cotton, squash, beans, and corn. They made pottery. They watched the stars, Moon, and Sun. The Anasazi lived in another area of the desert state. They lived in large groups called Pueblos. They made baskets. For some unknown reason, both groups disappeared. Scientists do not know what happened. Much later, other native tribes moved into the same areas. They lived like the Hohokam and the Anasazi.

The Spanish began exploring the area of present-day Arizona in the 1500s. They traveled up from Mexico. The first group came looking for gold. Others came to teach Native Americans Christianity and the Spanish way

of life. Finally, in 1752 the first settlement was built. It was a fort. One native group, the Apache, did not like the settlers on their land. The Apache began attacking.

In the early 1800s, the people of Mexico fought with Spain. They won. They now owned all the land that Spain had claimed. Many people from the United States traveled across the land on their way to California. Some stayed in the northern part of the Mexican territory. However, they did not want to follow Mexican laws. The United States and Mexico fought over the land. In 1848, the United States won. It got the part of Arizona that was north of the Gila River. Settlers moving west still traveled to the south of the river. In five years, the United States bought more land to the south of the river. Many people thought buying the land was a waste of money. They said it was just a desert. People called the area the "Wild West."

The Arizona Area!

By 1860, Arizona wanted to become a territory. The Civil War was just beginning. The Confederacy, the Southern states that had left the United States, wanted Arizona to become their territory. The Union said no. It wanted Arizona to be its territory. Arizona became a territory in the United States in 1862.

Many people moved to the new territory to ranch. There were many fights with Native Americans. After the Civil War, troops were sent to keep the settlers safe. By 1886, the great Apache chief Geronimo was caught. Most of the fighting between the groups stopped. The natives were moved to reservations. Reservations were pieces of land on which the Native Americans had to live on. Most of the land was far away from their hunting grounds.

Silver, gold, and copper were found in Arizona Territory. Settlers moved quickly into the area. Towns grew up overnight. Railroads followed. The tracks crossed from the east to the west. They passed through Arizona Territory. Peace and quiet was kept by the local lawmen. Gunfights took place often. In 1912, Arizona became the 48th state.

Water had always been a problem for the settlers. The new state decided it was time to build dams. When the rest of the United States was in the Great Depression, Arizona was working. The Depression was a time when people in the nation had no jobs and no money. Many people came to the state looking for jobs. The dams helped irrigate the land. Water could flow through the desert. Farmers found it a great place to grow cotton and fruit trees.

During the world wars, the government built air bases in the state. The land was perfect to practice flying airplanes and for desert training. The invention of air-conditioning in the 1950s was even more important. Arizona began to look for other new inventions. The state became known for using new machines and robots—  high-tech equipment. Many companies began to build in the state. By the 1990s, many people had moved to Arizona for jobs and training in these companies. The state had bloomed from dry, sandy desert to a state full of busy cities.

ARIZONA – *The Grand Canyon State*

The Arizona Area!

Landscape

Arizona has two kinds of landscape. About two fifths of the state is in the Colorado Plateau area. In this part are steep cliffs, plateaus, and deep canyons. The Grand Canyon, one of the Seven Natural Wonders of the World, is in part of Arizona. The rest of the state lies in the Basin and Range area. Basins and ranges are surrounded by tall mountains. The basins are usually deserts and very dry.

Climate

The climate in Arizona varies greatly. Most areas have little rain or snow. However, some mountain areas may have up to 30 inches per year. The average temperature in the desert areas in July is in the 90s. It is not unusual to have days that reach 130° F. The rest of the state is in the 80s. Temperatures in January across the state range from 0° to 50° F.

Natural Resources

While the land may seem dry and a desert, it is a natural resource. The deep canyons and steep mountains are beautiful. The state has set aside land for many parks. Arizona is also known for mining. At one time gold and silver were important minerals. Now, copper, sand, and gravel are important resources.

Economy

Modern technology is very important in Arizona. Many high-tech companies have built in the state. They make such products as computers, software for the computers, and space satellites. Service is another growing industry. In service jobs, people help other people. Many people like to visit Arizona. There is much to see, from the Grand Canyon to Native American powwows. People who have service jobs work in restaurants, talk on tours, or work on air-force bases. A small part of money is made in ranching sheep and cattle and farming crops, such as cotton and fruit.

ARIZONA – *The Grand Canyon State*

The Arizona Area!

Higher Education

Education is very important to Arizona. The state needs a large group of people who can work in the high-tech industries. Arizona State University and the University of Arizona were both started when Arizona was a territory. The University of Arizona is known for a museum that houses many kinds of Native American things. The Navajo College was the first school to open on a reservation.

Famous People

Many famous people are from Arizona. Geronimo was an Apache chief. He tried to keep settlers off the traditional Apache land. Wyatt Earp and Doc Holliday were famous lawmen in the Old West. They had a shoot-out with the Dalton gang at a famous ranch called the O. K. Corral. Many writers were interested in the fight. It led to a new kind of fiction writing called "Westerns." The artist Frederic Remington spent a lot of time in Arizona. He painted pictures and sculpted statues of cowboys. They looked very real.

Arizona Today

Arizona takes great pride in its history. Both the Native American and the cowboy ways of life are important to the state. Tourists visit the Native American reservations to learn about the traditional dances, music, and art of the different tribes. Rodeos, which first began as games of skill, are popular events. There is a great variety of industries in the state. Arizona continues to lead the way in the development of new technology. However, Arizona faces two major problems. When there are many people and companies in a city, there is often a problem with pollution. Arizona was at one time known for its clean air. People with breathing problems, like asthma, would move to the state. Now people are passing laws to make sure the air stays clean. The biggest problem Arizona faces is the water situation. The state uses pipes to carry water long distances from rivers to the cities. They also use water found underground. These water sources are not renewed quickly. Arizona must look for a lasting solution to keep the water flowing.

ARIZONA – *The Grand Canyon State*

Assessment

Circle the letter of the correct answer.

1. The capital of Arizona is _____.
   - **a.** Grand Canyon
   - **b.** Phoenix
   - **c.** Mesa
   - **d.** Yuma

2. The _____ built ditches to get water from rivers to their crops.
   - **a.** Spanish
   - **b.** Anasazi
   - **c.** cowboys
   - **d.** Hohokam

3. Before becoming a territory, Arizona was called _____.
   - **a.** the Wild West
   - **b.** O. K. Corral
   - **c.** Desert Dry
   - **d.** No Man's Land

4. The invention that changed the state was the _____.
   - **a.** computer
   - **b.** air conditioner
   - **c.** dams
   - **d.** water hose

5. The _____ is one of the Seven Natural Wonders of the World.
   - **a.** Gila River
   - **b.** Hopi Reservation
   - **c.** desert
   - **d.** Grand Canyon

6. The biggest problem Arizona faces is _____.
   - **a.** air pollution
   - **b.** loss of high-tech companies
   - **c.** lack of water
   - **d.** too many cattle

ARIZONA – *The Grand Canyon State*

Travel Time!

Pack Your Bags!

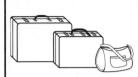

You will need:
- a United States road map   • Internet

The Hopi Indians live on a reservation in northern Arizona. Hopi means "peaceful people." Each August the Hopi perform the snake dance. Dancers wear masks and costumes. Men hit drums in a rhythm that has been passed down for centuries. It takes nine days to perform the ceremony. Visitors can only watch the dancers on the last day. Even then, the visitors must have permission. Research to find out more information about the snake dance.

On the Road!

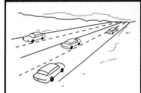

Suppose you have been given permission to watch the snake dance. Now you must get to the reservation in Arizona. Make a plan to get there on another sheet of paper. Use the road map to plan the route you will take to get there from your home. The information below will help you plan your trip.
- If you drive an average speed of 60 miles per hour for seven hours each day, how long will it take you to get there?
- Will you camp or stay in hotels?
- How much money will you need?

Snapshots!

Write a journal entry about what you think the snake dance will be like. Draw a picture to go with your writing.

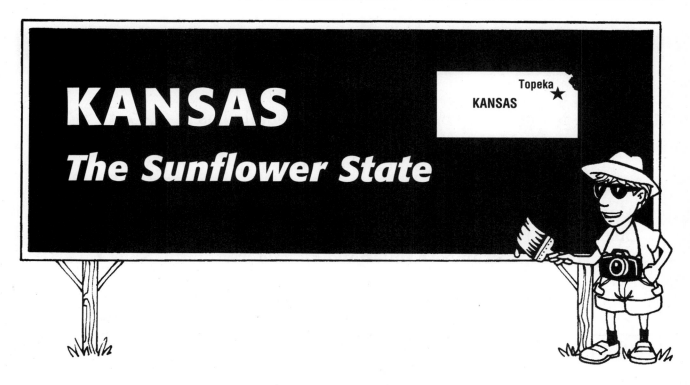

State Your Facts!

Capital: Topeka

Abbreviation: KS

Statehood: January 29, 1861— the 34th state

Motto: *Ad Astra per Aspera* ("To the Stars Through Difficulty")

Bird: Western meadowlark

Flower: Sunflower

Tree: Cottonwood

Area: 82,282 sq mi (213,110 sq km)—15th in size

Five largest cities: Wichita, Kansas City, Topeka, Overland Park, Lawrence

Highest point: Mount Sunflower—4,039 ft (1,231 m)

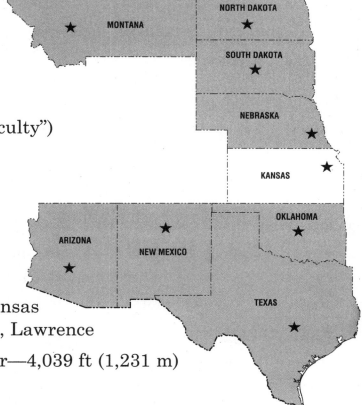

Things To Do!

1. A globe is like a map on a ball. A globe usually has a distance scale in its key. But it is hard to use a ruler to measure distance on a globe. The map curves like a ball. Use a piece of string instead. Measure how far your town is from the following places. Write your answers in the chart below. Give your answer in both miles and kilometers.

Place	Miles	Kilometers
Honolulu, Hawaii		
Anchorage, Alaska		
Bangor, Maine		
Miami, Florida		
Washington, D.C.		
Paris, France		
Sydney, Australia		
Cape Town, South Africa		
Rio de Janeiro, Brazil		

2. Research the history of the Kansas state flag. When was the flag first made? What things and colors are pictured on the flag? What do you think these things mean or stand for? Write a report about what you learn. Include a picture of the flag with your report.

3. Find out about an environmental problem in the state. Make a poster that tells about the problem. Include some pictures. How can the problem be fixed?

Come to Kansas!

Kansas is in the heartland of the United States. At times it has been at the center of American history.

History

People have lived in the Kansas area for almost 15,000 years. The earliest groups were known as Paleo-Indians. They hunted mammoths and other prehistoric beasts. Later, they formed villages and grew crops.

About 1,000 years ago, the Paleo-Indians split up into several groups. These included the Wichita, Kansa, Osage, and Pawnee. These groups also hunted and farmed for food. They lived in huts made of grass, mud, or clay. Later, other groups moved into the area. These new groups were the Kiowa, Cheyenne, Comanche, and Arapaho. These new Indian groups arrived on horses. Horses had been brought to North America by Spanish explorers in the 16th century.

In the 1540s, the Spanish explorer Coronado visited the area. He was seeking the Seven Cities of Cíbola. These cities were supposed to be made of gold. When Coronado reached Kansas, he gave up his search.

In the 1680s, the French explorer LaSalle claimed a large part of western North America for France. Kansas was part of that claim. By the 1740s, the French had built forts and trading posts in the Kansas area.

President Thomas Jefferson made a deal with France in 1803. The U.S. bought all of France's land holdings west of the Mississippi River. The price was $15 million. This deal was called the Louisiana Purchase. Kansas was part of the deal. In 1804, Meriwether Lewis and William Clark passed through Kansas. They had been sent by President Jefferson to explore the Louisiana Purchase.

In 1806, the American explorer Zebulon Pike visited the area. On his maps, he labeled the Kansas area as the "Great American Desert." The U.S. government then decided no settlers would live there. So it planned to move American Indian groups onto the land.

KANSAS – The Sunflower State

Come to Kansas!

Beginning in 1830, the U.S. government forced over 30 American Indian groups to move to Kansas. The land and climate were harsh for most of these people. They did not know how to feed or house themselves in this strange land. Many of the Indians died on the brutal journey there.

In the 1850s, slavery became a problem in Kansas. The Missouri Compromise, passed by Congress in 1820, had limited slavery. It said no state north of Missouri could enter the Union as a slave state. In 1854, the Kansas-Nebraska Act changed that. This act said each territory could vote whether to allow slavery.

The Kansas Territory soon became a battleground over slavery. People for and against slavery moved there. Each group wanted more people to support its side. Soon the arguments became violent. Men from Missouri who were for slavery crossed over into Kansas. They attacked people who were against slavery. Fighting became fierce and frequent. The territory soon became known as "Bleeding Kansas."

The vote about slavery in Kansas was finally held in 1858. People came into the state to vote illegally. The number of votes in the election was twice the population of the state! The side for slavery won. Slavery was legal in Kansas. New laws were passed. One law said that anyone who helped a slave to escape could be sentenced to death.

Fights in Kansas continued. Lawrence was the site of a terrible fight. Part of the town was destroyed in the riots. About 200 people were killed in Bleeding Kansas from 1854 to 1861.

Kansas entered the Union in January 1861 as a free state. But the Union was falling apart. Southern states had seceded, or withdrawn from the Union. In April 1861, the Civil War began. Few Civil War battles took place in Kansas. But one of the most brutal battles happened in Lawrence. William Quantrill was a renegade Confederate soldier. He formed his own band of soldiers, called Quantrill's Raiders. In 1863, they burned the town of Lawrence.

Come to Kansas!

They killed about 150 people there. Most of the victims were not soldiers.

After the Civil War, many settlers moved to Kansas. The Homestead Act of 1862 gave 160 acres of land to people for only $10. They had to promise to work the land for five years. These people became known as homesteaders.

Railroads also arrived in Kansas in the 1860s. Abilene, Dodge City, and Wichita became big "cow towns." Ranchers from Texas drove their cattle to these towns. The cattle were then shipped by rail to the East. These towns were known as wild places with little law and order. Famous sheriffs such as Wyatt Earp and Wild Bill Hickok kept the peace there. By the end of the century, railroads had reached Texas. The time of the great cattle drives was over.

As more settlers moved into Kansas, the Indian groups were moved out. The U.S. government made them move to Oklahoma. Times were hard for the new settlers. Many crops did not grow well on the plains. Then the

farmers started growing wheat. Kansas became known as the "Breadbasket of the World."

To grow more wheat, farmers cut down many of the trees. But then dry weather hit the state in the 1930s. The prairie winds blew away the soil. The land became like a desert. Crops would not grow, and the farms failed. Much of the state became part of the Dust Bowl. Even worse, the Great Depression also struck the state in the 1930s. Banks closed, and businesses failed. People lost their jobs. World War II helped Kansas to recover. Wheat was grown again. The economy improved.

In the 1950s, a famous court case started in Kansas. A young African-American girl, Linda Brown, was not allowed to attend an all-white school. The case was called *Brown versus Board of Education of Topeka, Kansas*. The case went all the way to the U.S. Supreme Court. The Supreme Court said that the races could not be separated in public schools. The

Come to Kansas!

Court ruled that such separation was unconstitutional.

Kansas now has good schools, a good economy, and people who like their freedom. The state has come a long way from a place called the "Great American Desert."

Landscape

Kansas is a medium-sized state. It measures about 206 miles (331 km) from north to south. It is about 408 miles (656 km) wide. The state is mostly a wide plain, but it is not level. Its high point, about 4,000 feet, is in the northwest corner of the state. The plain slopes to the state's low point in the southeast corner.

The eastern third of the state has hills but little level land. The central third has much level land and some hills. The western third is part of the High Plains. Major rivers in the state are the Kansas River and the Arkansas River. The Missouri River forms part of the

northeast border of Kansas. There are no large natural lakes in the state. But there are several man-made lakes and reservoirs.

Climate

Kansas is an inland state. It is not near any large bodies of water that help to moderate weather. So the state has extremes of weather. Temperatures can be very cold in the winter. They can be very hot in the summer. Rainfall ranges from 40 inches a year in the southeast to 15 inches in the west. The growing season varies from 150 to 185 days.

Natural Resources

Parts of Kansas have the rich glacier deposits known as loess. This soil is very good for farming. The state also has large deposits of oil, coal, and natural gas. Salt, zinc, and lead are also mined there. Helium is an important gas found in the state.

Economy

People in Kansas have many job choices. Farming is important in the state. Kansas leads the

KANSAS – The Sunflower State

nation in wheat production. Other farms grow corn, soybeans, and cattle. Factories in Kansas make airplanes and railroad cars. They make mobile homes and other things, too. Mining is also an important industry in the state.

Most people in Kansas have service jobs. Service people work to help other people. They work in banks, stores, and hospitals. They also help the many tourists that visit Kansas each year.

Higher Education

Kansas has many fine colleges to attend. The University of Kansas was created in 1863. Its main campus is in Lawrence. Kansas State University was also founded in 1863. It is centered in Manhattan.

Famous People

Many famous people have called Kansas home. Dwight D. Eisenhower lived there for many years. He became the 34th U.S. President. Bob Dole is another famous politician from the state.

Many artists and entertainers came from Kansas. The famous clown Emmett Kelly was born there. Charlie "Bird" Parker was a famous jazz musician from Kansas. William Inge and Gwendolyn Brooks were famous writers from the state. The great baseball pitcher Walter Johnson also came from there.

Kansas Today

Kansas has had many troubles in its history. But its people have overcome those problems. Now they look to the future with hope, just as their motto suggests.

Name _____ Date _____

Assessment

Circle the letter of the correct answer.

1. The Kiowa and Cheyenne Indians arrived in Kansas on _____.
   a. trains   **b.** horses
   c. boats   **d.** buffalo

2. Explorer Zebulon Pike called the Kansas area _____.
   a. a great place to live   **b.** Oklahoma
   c. home   **d.** the Great American Desert

3. Fights over slavery earned Kansas the name _____.
   a. Fight City   **b.** Breadbasket of the World
   c. Bleeding Kansas   **d.** the Wild West

4. Many people who moved to Kansas to claim land were called _____.
   a. homesteaders   **b.** Sooners
   c. Quantrill's Raiders   **d.** Confederates

Read each statement. Answer *true* or *false*.

_____ 5. Spanish explorers brought horses to the New World.

_____ 6. Kansas entered the Union as a slave state.

_____ 7. William Quantrill was a Union soldier.

_____ 8. Wyatt Earp and Wild Bill Hickok were sheriffs in Kansas.

_____ 9. *Brown versus Board of Education of Topeka, Kansas*, was a famous court case.

Travel Time!

Come to Kansas for vacation fun! Kansas has a rich history. So many of its vacation spots are linked to history. Wichita has Cow Town. It recreates what Wichita was like in the late 1800s. You can visit Wyatt Earp's jail there. Wichita is in south-central Kansas. Dodge City also has features from the "Wild West." You can visit Boot Hill or ride a horse-drawn stagecoach. Dodge City is in southwest Kansas. Abilene also has "cow town" attractions. It's in central Kansas.

Are you familiar with the books by Laura Ingalls Wilder? You can visit the Little House on the Prairie. It's located near Independence, in southeast Kansas. The Mid-America All-Indian Center and Museum is in Wichita. Eisenhower Center honors President Dwight Eisenhower. He was President in the 1950s. His center is located in Abilene.

Maybe you'd enjoy the Kickapoo Indian Powwow. It's held each July in Horton. Horton is in northeast Kansas. The Neewollah Festival is held in Independence each October. For music, try the Walnut Valley Bluegrass Festival. It's held in Winfield each September. Winfield is in south-central Kansas. For camping and boating fun, try El Dorado State Park. It's near El Dorado, in south-central Kansas.

Kansas also has some unusual places to visit. Do you remember the movie *The Wizard of Oz*? You can visit Dorothy's house. It is located in Liberal, in southwest Kansas. The middle of the contiguous United States is in Kansas. You can visit the Geographic Center of the U.S. It is located in Lebanon. This is in north-central Kansas. The Big Brutus Coal Shovel is a big attraction. It can be found near West Mineral. The Kansas Cosmosphere and Space Center is another unusual place. It's in Hutchinson, in central Kansas.

Do you like races? Get your fill of track and field at the Kansas Relays. They are held in Lawrence each April. Lawrence is in eastern Kansas. How about the National Midget Car Races? They're held in Belleville each August. Belleville is in north-central Kansas. And who could forget the International Pancake Race? It's held in Liberal each February.

KANSAS – *The Sunflower State*

Travel Time!

Pack Your Bags!

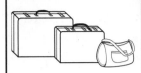

- You have ten days to travel around Kansas. Would you like to camp out, visit historic sites, or what? First, make a list of things you would like to do. Then make a list of places in Kansas you can do those things.
- Now plan a schedule for each of the ten days. Where will you go? What route will you take? Find a road map of Kansas. Use it to plan your routes. Where will you stay? Will you camp out or stay in hotels?
- Plan a budget for each day. How much do you think you will have to spend each day on your vacation? What would be the total cost for your ten-day trip?

On the Road!

- As you are driving, find words on signs or buildings that begin with the letters in your name. Write your name vertically on a piece of paper, one letter on each line. Then write the words you find by each letter.

Snapshots!

- Write a short story or poem about what life must have been like in the old cow towns of the late 1800s.
- Pretend that you were a young person moving west in a covered wagon. Would you be excited or scared? Write a diary entry about one day on your journey west.
- Draw a picture of the cyclone lifting Dorothy's house as it did in *The Wizard of Oz*.

KANSAS – *The Sunflower State*

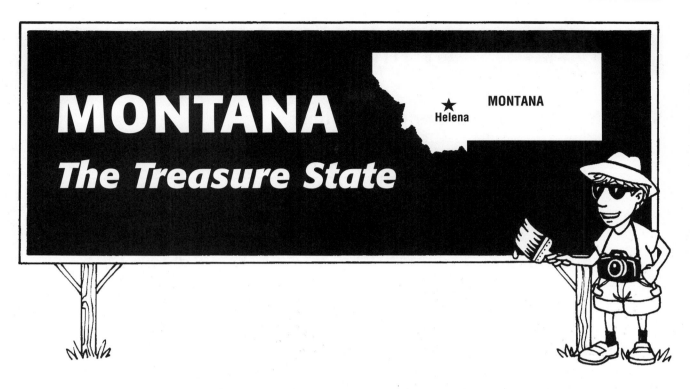

MONTANA
The Treasure State

=== **State Your Facts!** ===

Capital: Helena

Abbreviation: MT

Statehood: November 8, 1889—
the 41st state

Motto: *Oro y Plata* ("Gold and Silver")

Bird: Western meadowlark

Flower: Bitterroot

Tree: Ponderosa pine

Area: 147,047 sq mi
(380,849 sq km)—4th in size

Five largest cities: Billings,
Great Falls, Butte, Missoula,
Helena

Highest point: Granite Peak—12,799 ft (3,901 m)

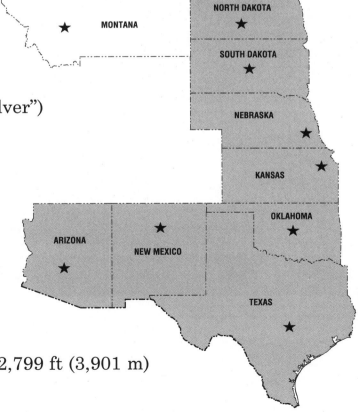

Name _____ Date _____

Things To Do!

Study the map. Then answer the questions.

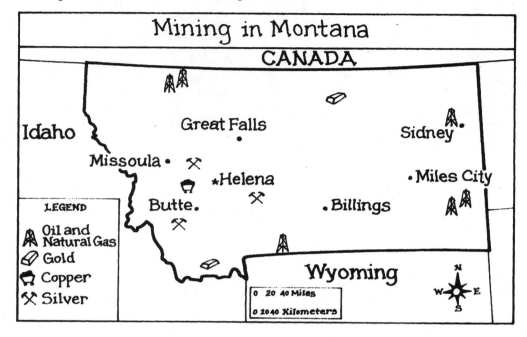

Mining in Montana

CANADA

Idaho

Great Falls

Missoula •

★Helena

Butte •

LEGEND

⚒ Oil and Natural Gas
✏ Gold
⚱ Copper
⚒ Silver

Sidney •

• Miles City

• Billings

Wyoming

0 20 40 Miles
0 20 40 Kilometers

N
W   E
S

1. What is mined near Sidney, Montana?

_____

2. Where is copper mined?

_____

3. Is silver mined near Miles City?

_____

4. Which mineral is found in most of the state? Explain.

_____

_____

Meeting Montana!

The Spanish explored the land of Montana. They called it the "Land of the Shining Mountains" because the sun would shine and sparkle on the white mountain peaks. However, the Spanish did not spend much time in the area. They did not see the wide open plains. They did not meet all of Montana!

History

Many Native American nations lived in the Montana area. Those living on the plains farmed beans, corn, and tobacco. They hunted buffalo. When the explorers came, the Native Americans traded buffalo hides, jewelry, and crops for horses. With the horses, the natives could easily follow the buffalo. Native groups living in the mountains hunted, fished, and gathered nuts and seeds. They, too, followed the buffalo across the plains when they got horses.

The French and Spanish both explored the area of present-day Montana. The French traveled down from Canada. They claimed the land for France. The Spanish came up from Mexico. But they did not try to claim the land. Until the United States bought the land in the deal known as the Louisiana Purchase, little was known about the area. Meriwether Lewis and William Clark were hired by President Thomas Jefferson to map the western part of the United States in 1804. The team got to Montana in 1805.

Fur trappers and traders began to hunt in the area. But they did not stay in one place very long. The first settlement was built in 1841 by a missionary. Few people moved to the new land. Most were heading to California and Oregon. However, as railroads spread from the East to the West, some people saw the beauty of Montana and decided to make it their home. They farmed the land.

A big gold find in Montana in 1852 started a rush to the area. Towns grew overnight. In about ten years, there were enough people in the area  to form a new territory. In 1864, the Montana Territory was formed.

Settlers heard stories of good farmland and rich gold mines. They poured into the new territory. Soon ranchers from Texas began herding their cattle north to the

MONTANA – *The Treasure State*

Meeting Montana!

Montana Territory. The cattle could feed on the rich grass. From there, cattle were moved to the Wyoming Territory, where  railroads spread out to all parts of the United States. The beef was sent quickly across the nation.

Native Americans became angry. Settlers took their land. Cattle roamed on their hunting grounds. Some tribes began to attack settlers and steal cattle. The army was called in to protect the settlers. One unit of 210 men was led by Lieutenant Colonel George Custer. In June 1876, Custer and his army fought a group of Native Americans made up of several tribes. Custer and all of his men were killed. The battle was known as the Battle of Little Big Horn. The people in the United States were angry. More troops were sent to the West. By 1880, the fighting was over in Montana Territory. The Native Americans were forced to live in areas that few people would settle. These land areas were reservations.

One year later, another mineral was found in Montana—copper. A new wave of people flooded the state. There were enough people in the state within eight years for Montana to become the 41st state.

As the state moved into the 1900s, it had a balance of businesses. There were ranchers, farmers, and a variety of mineral mines. All products were used in World War I. The Montana economy was booming. By 1918, a drought hit Montana and other plains states. There was no rain for several years. Crops died. The fields were all dust. Just as Montana began to recover, the Great Depression hit in the 1930s. People were out of work. Many banks and businesses closed. Another drought hit the land. People left Montana looking for jobs. The government tried to help. It made jobs that ran electric lines and irrigation pipes. As the United States entered World War II, Montana's mines, crops, and cattle ranches were needed once again to help the army.

Over the years, people have moved back to Montana. Today, nearly 47 percent of the people live in small communities. They enjoy the treasures Montana offers, from skiing to fishing to the big, open sky. They enjoy everything that is Montana.

Meeting Montana!

Landscape

Montana is divided into two areas. The plains cover about two thirds of the eastern part of the state. The land has rolling hills and wide river valleys. The land is covered in grasses. In the southwest plains, there are gully areas. Glaciers are large sheets of ice. Long ago, glaciers moved across some of Montana to shape it. The glaciers also made many holes. When part of the glaciers melted, water filled the holes to make lakes. The western part of the state is in the Rocky Mountains. They are steep, tall mountains. They are covered with trees. In the northwest, over 50 glaciers still fill the mountains in Glacier National Park.

Climate

Just as the land varies from the plains to the mountains, so does the climate. The plains have an average temperature of around 70° F in July and 25° F in January. Temperatures may be more than 20° cooler in the mountains. The spring and summer months get most of the rain. The mountains may receive up to 80 inches of snow and rain each year. The plains may get as little as ten inches.

Natural Resources

Montana's nickname is the "Treasure State." It gets its name because of the richness of its resources. There is a wealth of minerals. These include petroleum, copper, coal, gold, and silver. Forests cover about one fourth of the land. They are found in the mountains. Finally, there are many lakes and rivers that provide water for drinking, electricity, and outside fun.

Economy

The state has a very balanced economy. Its main source of money comes from service jobs. Many people work in jobs that help visitors. Others work in hospitals or on military bases. Farming and ranching are other important sources of money. Farmers raise wheat and sugar beets, and ranchers raise cattle, hogs, and sheep. Montana is also known for its mining of petroleum and gold, as well as manufacturing paper goods.

MONTANA – *The Treasure State*

Name _____ Date _____

Meeting Montana!

Higher Education

There are six colleges that together make up the college system in Montana. Montana State University is one of the oldest. It opened as a school that taught farming in 1893. Today it teaches a wide variety of subjects, from education to business.

Famous People

Charles Russell lived in Montana in the late 1800s. He was a cowboy and hunter. He painted pictures of scenes from the West. Some of his most famous pictures show cowboys sitting around a campfire or a Native American sitting on a horse. A. B. Guthrie, Jr., is a writer from Montana. He wrote the novel *The Big Sky*. It tells the history of Native Americans and trappers in the early 1800s.

Montana Today

Montana is a blend of Old West and new technology. Most towns are small. The people use new technology, such as the Internet, fax machines, and computers to keep in touch. Montana has already begun to look to its future, though. People there are willing to change to meet future needs, but not so much that their lives and their beautiful land are hurt. One group of people has traveled around the state, talking to the people in different towns. As a result, leaders in the Montana government have set three goals. First, they want a clean and safe place to live. Second, they want to make the education of students better. Finally, they want to make health care better. Some towns are so small that they do not have doctors or dentists. As Montana moves into the future, the people are planning carefully. Do you think they will meet their goals?

MONTANA – *The Treasure State*

Assessment

Write the correct words to complete the sentences.

1. The use of _____ helped Native Americans follow buffalo across the plains.

2. The United States bought the land rights of present-day Montana in the deal known as the _____.

3. Cattle ranchers from _____ herded their cattle to Montana Territory to feed on the rich grass.

4. In the Battle of Little Big Horn, _____ and his army were killed in a fight with several Native American tribes.

5. _____ dug holes in the land and then melted to make many of Montana's lakes.

6. Montana's nickname is the "Treasure State" because it has so many natural _____.

7. People who work in service jobs in Montana may help _____ who travel to the state.

8. _____ was a cowboy who painted pictures of the West.

9. One of Montana's goals is to make _____ better, because some towns do not have doctors or dentists.

MONTANA – *The Treasure State*

Travel Time!

Pack Your Bags!

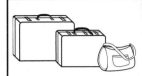

You will need:
- Internet
- resource books

Nelson Story was a Texas rancher. He heard about the rich grass in Montana Territory. He also knew it was easy to move things in the North because of many railroads. In 1867, Nelson Story decided to take his cattle to Montana. The cattle could eat grass for several months, then be moved to Cheyenne to the stockyards.

On the Road!

Suppose you have been hired by Mr. Story to herd the cattle from Texas to Montana. Research to find out what the trip might be like. The questions below will help you find important information!

- As a cowboy, what will you need?
- What states or territories will you go through as you ride from Texas to Montana Territory? How long will the trip take?
- What jobs will you have to do?

Snapshots!

- Write a journal entry telling about a day in the life of a cowboy herding cattle. Draw a picture to go with your writing.

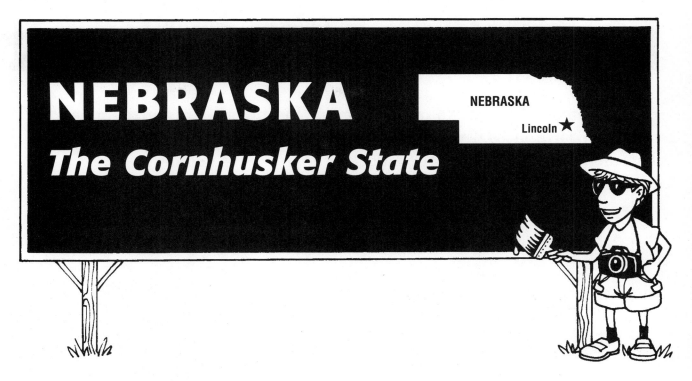

State Your Facts!

Capital: Lincoln

Abbreviation: NE

Statehood: March 1, 1867—the 37th state

Motto: "Equality Before the Law"

Bird: Western meadowlark

Flower: Goldenrod

Tree: Cottonwood

Area: 77,359 sq mi (200,358 sq km)—15th in size

Five largest cities: Omaha, Lincoln, Grand Island, North Platte, Fremont

Highest point: area in Kimball County— 5,426 ft (1,654 m)

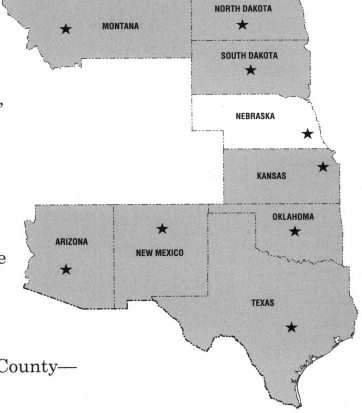

Things To Do!

This map of Nebraska is a grid map. To find the city for the given number coordinates, first find the letter along the left side of the map. Then move your finger to the right to the numbered column.

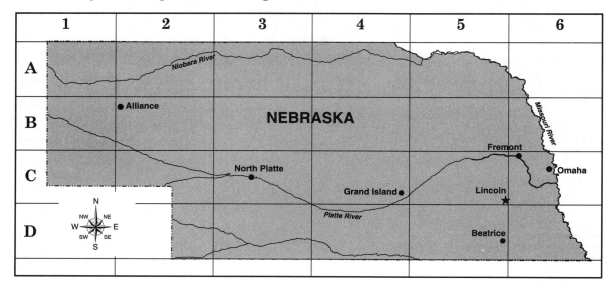

A. Name the city shown by each coordinate.

1. C, 6 _____

_____

2. B, 2 _____

3. C, 3 _____

4. C, 5 _____

5. C, 4 _____

6. D, 5 _____

B. A map has an index. It lists the cities in alphabetical order. The coordinates of the grid are listed beside each city name. Make an index of the cities shown on the map.

INDEX

_____   _____

_____   _____

_____   _____

_____

NEBRASKA – *The Cornhusker State*

Navigate Nebraska!

Many people heard the call of the West. They left home and family looking for land, riches, adventure—a new way of life. They often followed the Oregon Trail, a 2,000-mile trail that started in Missouri and ended in Oregon. Part of the trail followed the Platte River, a river that crossed dry, grassy plains. The settlers did not know it at the time, but they were navigating through present-day Nebraska, a state now known for its rich farmland.

History

Most of the Native Americans living in what is now Nebraska followed the buffalo. They used the animal to make clothing, hunting tools, and shelter. It was also their main food. Even the few native tribes that farmed along the rivers would hunt the buffalo two times each year.

The Spanish explored the New World in 1541. They traveled up from Mexico. They came as far as present-day Kansas. The Spanish claimed much of the land to the north for Spain. Nearly 150 years later, the French claimed the same land for their country. They did not explore the region, either. The first

European actually to visit present-day Nebraska was French. On his return, he told of a land rich in beaver. French trappers and traders quickly moved to the area. They traded with the natives along the rivers.

In a battle that lasted seven years, the Spanish got to claim all the land. The French soon got the rights back. By 1803, the United States bought all the land from the French. The deal was called the Louisiana Purchase. With the new land, the United States doubled in size. Moreover, the West could now be reached by traveling overland. Explorers were hired to find a path from the East to the West.

The easiest way followed the Platte River. The river ran from the east to the west border of Nebraska. The trail became known as the Oregon Trail. From 1843 to 1869, over 350,000 people followed the river in their move to California, Oregon, or Washington. Few settlers stayed in the dry plains of Nebraska. Only trappers and fur

NEBRASKA – The Cornhusker State

Navigate Nebraska!

traders remained in the area. Some Native American nations also had moved there. They had been pushed off their land earlier by settlers in Mississippi. Now they became angry at the large number of wagons and pioneers.

The Nebraska Territory was formed in 1854. It was a large region that included present-day Kansas and Nebraska. To settle the land, the government offered 160 acres to anyone who would live on and farm the land for five years. People from other countries and soldiers from the Civil War were looking for new lives. They quickly settled on the land. Soon there were enough people in the territory to divide the land and make two states. Nebraska was formed in 1867.

Railroads were built across the state. To feed the workers, hunters killed large numbers of buffalo. The loss of the buffalo herds and the growing number of people in the region forced the natives to move a third time. This time, they moved to areas farther northwest.

Beginning in 1870, a string of problems hit the Nebraska farmers. Grasshoppers ate crops. There was no rain for several years. Ranchers in the western part of the state did not like farmers building fences. But as the state moved into the 1900s, the government helped pay for irrigation, a way to water crops using pipes to carry water from rivers to the farms. Farming became easier.

Nebraska became an important state during World War I. Its crops and cattle were used to feed the armies fighting overseas. However, Nebraska farmers again faced major problems after the war. The Great Depression followed the war in 1930. People were out of work. Banks and businesses closed. Farmers could not pay their loans. Many lost their farms. Those that still held land were faced with another drought. The governor of the state stopped banks from closing the farms. Also, the United States government gave low-interest loans.

In 1937, Nebraska tried a new form of government. Instead of having a Senate and House of Representatives form of legislature, the people voted to have only one house. Laws could now be passed more quickly. There would be fewer people talking about the laws that needed to be passed.

NEBRASKA – *The Cornhusker State*

Navigate Nebraska!

Since 1937, Nebraskans have continued to move forward slowly. They keep the pioneer spirit alive as they face the ups and downs of farming and ranching. Even after the Missouri River flooded in 1993, the farmers were able to rebuild and plant the following year with the help of the government.

Landscape

Most of Nebraska is flat or gently rolling. The soil is sandy. Rain soaks into the ground right away. Because of this, there is little erosion to make rivers or streams. In the center of the state is an area know as the Sandy Hills. The land is sandy and forms dunes, hills of sand. Grasses cover the dunes when there is rain. In dry seasons, there is no grass. Wind moves the dunes. Rivers cross the state. Most have their source in the Rocky Mountains. As snow melts, the water flows east. Along the rivers, there may be marshes and green valleys.

Climate

Because the land is open and mostly flat, the climate in Nebraska is harsh. Winters are cold and snowy. Snow covers the state for up to two months during the winter. The average temperature is about 20° F. Summers are hot. Temperatures in July can climb above 100° F. June is the wettest month.

Natural Resources

There are few forests or minerals in Nebraska. Trees that are there were planted by early settlers. The grasses that grow so well are a kind of natural resource. They make the soil rich for growing crops. Water is also a resource. Several main rivers flow through the state and along its borders. The Sandy Hills also have many lakes.

Economy

Farming and ranching have always been important to the state. Ranchers raise cattle, hogs, and sheep. Farmers raise corn, soybeans, and oats. Raising the food also leads to another industry in Nebraska. Companies take the farm goods and turn them into packaged food. Other kinds of manufacturing include electric equipment and machinery. As in most states, Nebraska's main source of money comes from people who work in

NEBRASKA – The Cornhusker State

Navigate Nebraska!

service jobs. These people help people instead of making a product. Insurance is a main service job in the state. However, the fastest growing service job is tourism. Nebraska has rebuilt many historic places to show what life was like in the 1800s. Visitors like to see how people lived in those times.

Higher Education

Education has been very important to the people of Nebraska. When the area was just a territory, the government formed 27 schools for higher learning. Only one of these schools, Peru State College, is still open today. This school teaches classes in such courses as education and business. The University of Nebraska is one of the largest universities. It was formed in 1869. The first classes were taught in 1871. Today it has several locations around the state. It teaches such subjects as medicine, business, and agriculture.

Famous People

One of Nebraska's most famous people is Willa Cather. She moved to Nebraska when she was nine years old. She wrote about people who lived on the prairie. She won a Pulitzer Prize for her story *One of Ours*. Susette La Flesche was a writer and a painter. She was the daughter of a chief of the Omaha nation. Her Native American name was *Inshta Theumba*. The famous Buffalo Bill Cody lived in Nebraska during his adult years. He hunted buffalo to feed the workers laying the railroad tracks. He also put together a traveling show. He had people in the show that did tricks on horses, were sharpshooters, or did rope tricks. Buffalo Bill was the person who started rodeos.

Nebraska Today

Water is the key to Nebraska's future. There seems to be plenty of water now with rivers and underground wells. However, the underground wells may not last. Nebraska is looking well into the future to find new ways to farm and new crops that do not need as much water to grow. Nebraska people are hard workers. They will surely do well, just as they have in the past.

Name _____ Date _____

Assessment

Read each statement. Answer _true_ or _false_.

_____ 1. Forests are an important natural resource
for Nebraska.

_____ 2. The French and Spanish both claimed
the land of present-day Nebraska for
their countries.

_____ 3. The Oregon Trail followed the Platte River
north to south across Nebraska.

_____ 4. From the very beginning of the state's
history, people wanted to move to Nebraska.

_____ 5. The legislature in Nebraska has one house
instead of two—the House of Representatives
and the Senate.

_____ 6. Farming is the greatest source of money
for the state.

_____ 7. Buffalo Bill Cody started rodeos.

_____ 8. Nebraska has mountains, deserts,
and canyons.

NEBRASKA – _The Cornhusker State_

Travel Time!

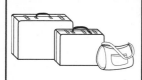

Pack Your Bags!

You will need:
• Nebraska road map

On the Road!

Several states border Nebraska. Plan a road trip inside Nebraska that would take you to each state. The questions below will help you plan the trip.
• Which states border Nebraska?
• Which roads will take you along the borders of Nebraska?
• How far will you drive? Calculate the road miles you will travel.

Snapshots

Compare your route with several other classmates. How many different ways could you visit all the states?

_____

_____

_____

_____

_____

_____

NEW MEXICO
The Land of Enchantment

Santa Fe ★
NEW MEXICO

State Your Facts!

Capital: Santa Fe

Abbreviation: NM

Statehood: January 6, 1912—
the 47th state

Motto: *Crescit Eundo* ("It Grows as
It Goes")

Bird: Roadrunner

Flower: Yucca

Tree: Piñon

Area: 121,593 sq mi
(314,295 sq km)—5th in size

Five largest cities: Las Cruces,
Santa Fe, Roswell, Albuquerque, Farmington

Highest point: Wheeler Park—13,161 ft (4,011 m)

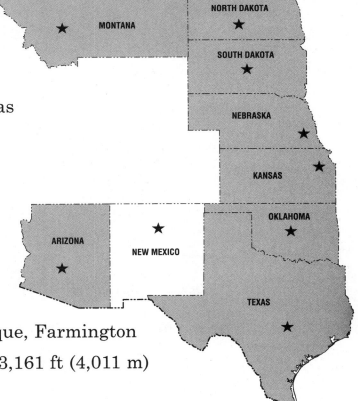

Name _____ Date _____

Things To Do!

Use the map to answer the questions below.

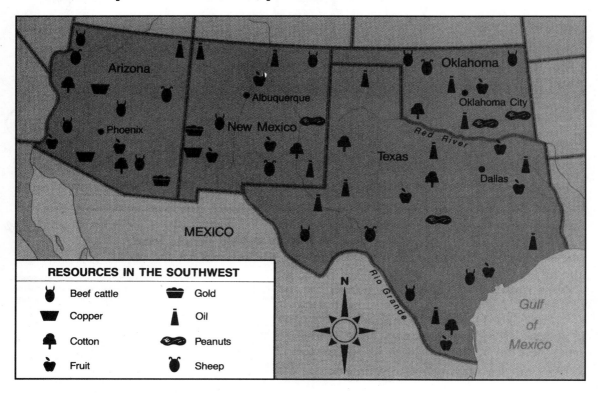

1. What is the name of this map? _____

2. In which states is gold found? _____

3. Is there more oil in Arizona or Texas? _____

4. Cotton can be found in the four states shown on the map.
   Name two other resources that can be found in all four states.

   _____

5. Which state does not grow peanuts? _____

6. In which two states is copper found? _____

7. What state is west of New Mexico? _____

8. What country is south of the states shown? _____

It's Enchanting in New Mexico!

New Mexico is a place of beautiful deserts and snowy mountains. Sunlight paints the rocks and landscape with vivid colors. With its rich history and promising future, New Mexico truly is the "Land of Enchantment."

History

People have lived in the New Mexico area for over 10,000 years. These early people lived in well-built villages. They made beautiful pottery and jewelry. The Navajo called these people the *Anasazi,* or "ancient ones." About 600 years ago, the Anasazi began to break into smaller groups. These American Indian groups became known as Pueblo Indians. These groups included the Zuni and Hopi.

Other American Indian groups also lived in the New Mexico area. These included the Comanche and the Apache. The Comanche and Apache were nomadic groups. They moved from place to place, often following the buffalo herds. The Comanche and Apache were warriors, and they often fought other groups. By 1500, another warrior group had arrived. These people were the Navajo. They lived in permanent villages. They learned to farm from the Pueblo.

Spanish explorers began to arrive in the 1520s. The first was Cabeza de Vaca. After shipwrecking in Texas, he explored the Southwest for eight years. Then his group returned to Mexico. De Vaca's soldiers told stories of the Seven Cities of Cíbola. They were supposed to be cities of gold.

Other Spanish explorers searched for these cities. In 1540, Father Marcos de Niza, a priest, led a group. They reached present-day New Mexico. Then the Zuni attacked them, and the group returned to Mexico. A few years later, Francisco de Coronado

It's Enchanting in New Mexico!

searched for the cities. His soldiers defeated the Zuni. Coronado did not find gold, either. He turned back when his group reached the Grand Canyon. But he did claim the area for Spain.

Around 1600, the Spanish started a colony in the New Mexico area. It was called San Juan des los Caballeros. Over the next 200 years, the Spanish fought the Indian groups. The Spanish wanted the Indians to become Christians. The Indians refused. The Comanche, Apache, and Navajo often attacked Spanish towns, too. Around 1790, the Spanish signed a treaty with the Comanche. Then the Comanche helped the Spanish fight the Apache and Navajo.

In 1821, Mexico gained its independence from Spain. New Mexico became a province of Mexico. Also in 1821, American trader William Becknell blazed the Santa Fe Trail. It was a trade

route that started in Independence, Missouri. It stretched all the way to Santa Fe. This trail opened the New Mexico area to trade with the United States.

In 1845, the U.S. admitted Texas to the Union. Part of Texas at the time was today's New Mexico. But Mexico still claimed the land, too. The dispute got worse, and the Mexican War began. In 1848, the U.S. won the war. The U.S. gained much southwestern and western land as a result. New Mexico was part of that land. In 1853, the U.S. bought more land from Mexico. The Gadsden Purchase included the southern part of New Mexico.

New Mexico became a territory in 1850. People there voted not to allow slavery. When the Civil War began in 1861, New Mexico sided with the Union. Confederate soldiers from Texas invaded New Mexico. They captured Albuquerque and Santa Fe. But in 1862, New Mexico soldiers defeated the Texans in a battle at Glorieta Pass.

It's Enchanting in New Mexico!

New Mexico had another problem during the Civil War. The Apache and Navajo started to attack towns again. The Indians were soon defeated. Then they were forced to move to Bosque Redondo. It was a dry, barren reservation in southeast New Mexico. Many Navajo died on the journey there. That trip became known as the "Long Walk."

In the 1870s, more settlers moved into the area. Some came looking for gold. Others started cattle and sheep ranches. By the 1880s, the railroads reached into New Mexico. The days of the outlaws and gunfighters, such as Billy the Kid, were drawing to a close, too.

In 1912, New Mexico became the 47th state. A drought struck the state in the 1920s. Many ranches failed. But oil was discovered in 1922. The economy began to improve. The good times did not last long. The Great Depression struck the state in the early 1930s. Banks closed, and businesses shut down. Many people lost their jobs. Another drought gripped the state in 1932. The soil turned to dust. Strong winds blew up dust clouds so thick they blocked the sunlight.

The United States entered World War II in 1941. New Mexico was the site of much weapons research. Rockets and missiles were tested there. The first atomic bomb was exploded near Los Alamos in 1945. Similar bombs were dropped on two Japanese cities later that year. Japan surrendered, and World War II ended.

During the 1950s and 1960s, New Mexico grew quickly. Its population increased by 30 percent. New test labs were built in the state. White Sands became an important research center. Many minerals were mined during this time, especially uranium. In the 1970s, many older people moved to New Mexico to retire. They enjoyed the dry climate and clean air. Many high-tech companies opened in the state. The state's population grew 28 percent during the 1970s.

Now New Mexico is an important center for space and nuclear research. With its beautiful landscape, it is also very popular with tourists.

Name _____   Date _____

It's Enchanting in New Mexico!

Landscape

New Mexico is one of the larger states. It measures 391 miles (629 km) north to south. It is about 352 miles (566 km) wide. The state is on a plateau. The highest point is in the north-central part of the state. The land slopes away to the south.

New Mexico has many mountains. One group is the Rocky Mountains. They run from north to south in the central part of the state. Other groups are the Jemez Mountains and the Guadalupe Mountains. Many caves can be found in the state. The most famous is Carlsbad Caverns.

The main rivers in New Mexico are the Rio Grande and the Canadian River. The large lakes in the state are man-made. The continental divide passes through the western part of the state.

Climate

New Mexico has a dry climate. Rainfall ranges from 7 to 25 inches a year. Temperatures in the state can dip way below freezing in the winter. They can climb way above 100° F in the summer. Winds usually blow from the south and west.

Natural Resources

New Mexico has large deposits of oil and natural gas. Potash and uranium are also important minerals found there. Copper, gold, silver, and zinc are mined in the state. So are gypsum, perlite, salt, clay, and gemstones.

It's Enchanting in New Mexico!

Economy

New Mexico provides its people with a variety of jobs. Farming is a small part of the economy. Cattle, sheep, wool, and hay are major farm products. Mining is an important industry in the state. New Mexico is the leading producer of potash in the nation. Potash is used to make fertilizers.

The state is home to many high-tech companies. Computer parts are made there. Other factories make medical products, food products, and concrete.

The U.S. government employs many people in the state. They work in the research centers there. Many other people have service jobs. They serve as doctors, cooks, or bankers. Many service workers help tourists who visit the state.

Higher Education

New Mexico has several fine colleges from which to choose. New Mexico State University was founded in 1888. Its home campus is in University Park, near Las Cruces. The University of New Mexico was created in 1889. It is centered in Albuquerque.

Famous People

Some famous people from history were from New Mexico. William Bonney, better known as Billy the Kid, lived and died there. Kit Carson, the legendary frontier scout, was also from the state. Famous artists have also lived there. The writer D.H. Lawrence lived near Taos for many years. Georgia O'Keeffe, the well-known painter, lived much of her life in the state.

New Mexico Today

New Mexico is a dry land, but it is a beautiful place. It has learned to balance its past and its future. The state will surely be a land of enchantment in the 21st century.

Assessment

Circle the letter of the correct answer.

1. Some of the first people in the New Mexico area were the ____.
   a. French
   b. Anasazi
   c. Spanish
   d. English

2. The Seven Cities of Cíbola were supposed to be made of ____.
   a. mud
   b. silver
   c. wood
   d. gold

3. Apache and Navajo Indians were sent to a reservation called ____.
   a. Bosque Redondo
   b. Glorieta Pass
   c. Santa Fe
   d. White Sands

4. Georgia O'Keeffe was a famous ____.
   a. writer
   b. outlaw
   c. painter
   d. explorer

Read each statement. Answer *true* or *false*.

_____ 5. The Comanche and Apache were nomadic warrior groups.

_____ 6. Mexico won the Mexican War.

_____ 7. New Mexico was part of the Confederacy in the Civil War.

_____ 8. Billy the Kid was a famous sheriff.

_____ 9. The first atomic bomb was exploded in New Mexico.

NEW MEXICO – *The Land of Enchantment*

Travel Time!

What's new to do in New Mexico? Many vacation spots in the state are linked to American Indian history. The Acoma Pueblo is a great place to start. This is an ancient city that sits on top of a mesa. Called "Sky City," it is more than 350 feet above the valley floor. The Acoma Pueblo is about 50 miles southwest of Albuquerque in central New Mexico. The Gila Cliff Dwellings are another example of unusual homes. They are located north of Silver City, in southwest New Mexico.

Bandelier National Monument is just south of Los Alamos. This park in north-central New Mexico features the remains of an ancient civilization. There you can see cave and cliff dwellings deep in Frijoles Canyon.

Gallup is known as the "Indian Capital of the World." There you can see all kinds of arts and crafts by Navajos and other groups. Gallup is in western New Mexico. Taos is another well-known art center. There you can find artwork from three cultures— Indian, Spanish-American, and Anglo-American. The town features adobe buildings. Nearby is snow skiing. Taos is in north-central New Mexico.

Albuquerque and Santa Fe feature the Spanish history of New Mexico. Albuquerque has a Spanish-style "Old Town." It's located in central New Mexico. Santa Fe is northeast of Albuquerque. There you can see the Palace of the Governors. It was built in 1609. It is the oldest public building in the U.S. The capital building there is unusual. It was built to resemble a Pueblo Indian kiva. A *kiva* is an adobe structure that is partly underground.

Maybe you want to go completely underground. Then head to Carlsbad Caverns National Park. It's in southeast New Mexico, near the border with Texas. One tour in the cave is three miles long. You can visit an underground room that is over 200 feet high!

For outdoor fun, try Pecos Wilderness Area. It contains two national forests. You can backpack or ride horses there. Lakes and streams offer good fishing. You can also see Rocky Mountain bighorn

NEW MEXICO – *The Land of Enchantment*

sheep there. This area is in north-central New Mexico. Also in north-central New Mexico is Rio Grande Gorge State Park. A scenic bridge offers views of the gorge. The park has picnic areas and horse trails. You can also hike and camp there.

If you have more vacation time, visit Albuquerque in October. The Kodak International Balloon Fiesta is held there. Hundreds of hot-air balloons are featured. And who could miss the Great American Duck Race? It's held in Deming each August. Deming is in southwest New Mexico.

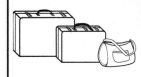

Pack Your Bags!

- Plan a trip to Albuquerque for your family. How far is your home from Albuquerque? How many days would you like to stay there? What other things could you do in the area? What would you want to do each day? Make a schedule for each day. Then make an estimate of how much your trip would cost. Include total costs for these things: travel costs, hotel costs, food costs, and admission costs.

On the Road!

- As you are driving, find words on signs or buildings that begin with the letters in *New Mexico*. Write *New Mexico* vertically on a piece of paper, one letter on each line. Then write the words you find by each letter. See who can find words for all the letters first.

Snapshots!

- Make a model of a pueblo or cliff dwelling.
- Draw a picture of a cave. Include stalagmites and stalactites.

NORTH DAKOTA
The Flickertail State

NORTH DAKOTA
★
Bismarck

State Your Facts!

Capital: Bismarck

Abbreviation: ND

Statehood: November 2, 1889—
the 39th state

Motto: "Liberty and Union; Now and
Forever; One and Inseparable"

Bird: Western meadowlark

Flower: Wild prairie rose

Tree: American elm

Area: 70,704 sq mi
(183,123 sq km)—17th in size

Five largest cities: Fargo,
Grand Rapids, Bismarck, Minot, Dickinson

Highest point: White Butte—3,506 ft (1,069 m)

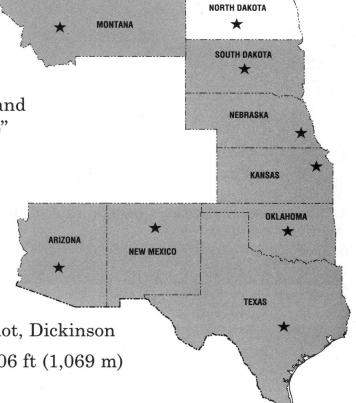

Things To Do!

A. Draw the following places on the map.

1. Rivers:

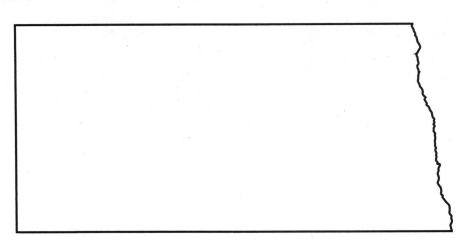

Missouri River
Sheyenne River
Red River
James River
Souris River
Cannonball River
Heart River
Lake Sakakawea

2. Sites:

White Butte
Theodore Roosevelt National Park

3. Cities:

Bismarck
Fargo
Grand Forks

B. Research the following questions.
Write a brief paragraph to answer each.

4. How did North Dakota get its nickname, the "Flickertail State"?

5. What do the pictures on the state seal mean? Draw the seal.

6. Where is the geographic center of North America?

North, But Central!

North Dakota is a state that is far north in the United States. However, it is also the center of the North American continent.

History

The Native Americans living in the area of present-day North Dakota lived along the lakes and rivers. They grew crops, such as corn and beans. They hunted buffalo and deer. Some groups made their houses out of clay and mud.

The French were the first Europeans to claim the area in 1682. Most of the land was part of Louisiana Territory. A small corner of the northeastern area was part of Hudson Bay Territory. This small area was given to Great Britain 20 years later. French explorers did not actually visit the area until 1738. It would still be another 50 years before people began to travel in the area. Trappers and fur traders found many beavers.

The United States bought Louisiana Territory from the French in 1803. This large region reached from the Mississippi River to the Rocky Mountains. It included most of North Dakota. Meriwether Lewis and William Clark explored the new territory the next year. They reached North Dakota in October. Winter was coming. They built a fort to live in. They stayed in North Dakota that winter.

The first settlement was built in 1812 by settlers traveling from Canada. Soon, Great Britain and the United States argued about where the boundaries for the countries would be. They agreed that the boundary would be the 49th parallel.

Dakota Territory was formed in 1861. To get settlers to move to the new territory, the government gave 160 acres of land to anyone who would live on the land and farm it for five years. The offer was called the Homestead Act. The people were called homesteaders. Settlers were slow to move to Dakota Territory. There were raids by native tribes, and there were few roads to get to the new territory.

Starting in 1872, the government gave land to railroad companies. The companies built towns along the tracks. To get people to live in the towns, they wrote about the places in newspapers in other countries.

NORTH DAKOTA – The Flickertail State

North, But Central!

Immigrants came from all over the world to live in Dakota Territory. *Immigrants* were people who traveled from one country to make their home in a new country. Many of these immigrants were farmers. Wheat was a favorite crop. It grew so well that many people heard about it. Many people began to move quickly to Dakota Territory. Cattle ranchers also bought land to graze their cattle on.

Railroad companies were in competition to move the grain and beef across the land. As a result, the companies built even more railroads across the territory. Most tracks ran east to west. Few ran north to south. The people in Dakota Territory asked that the region be divided in two. Since there were so many people now, the United States government decided to make the territory two states. On the same day, North Dakota and South Dakota joined the United States. North Dakota joined first since its name came first in the alphabet.

Most of the railroad companies were owned by people living in other states. These people often made the rules and owned the banks. People in North Dakota wanted more say in their businesses. They started a group called the Nonpartisan League. The people worked together to build banks, grain elevators, and storage areas for beef. They even started a service to give insurance to farmers for crop damage.

Times were good for the farmers and ranchers until 1930. The Great Depression hit. It was a time when banks closed, and people were out of work. Soon after, a drought hit the land. There was no rain. The soil was dry and got blown by the wind. Many people left North Dakota for jobs in other states. Those that stayed worked hard. Their efforts paid off in 1941. The soldiers in World War II needed their grain and beef. Then the government built a dam to help irrigate the fields. Irrigation meant that water would travel in pipes from rivers to the fields.

By the 1950s, the people of North Dakota began to look for new businesses to bring into the state. They found oil, natural gas, and

NORTH DAKOTA – *The Flickertail State*

North, But Central!

lignite, a kind of coal. The Air Force built bases in the state. Even when drought and flooding hit in later years, North Dakota was able to live through the rough times.

Landscape

North Dakota has three main land regions. The Red River Valley is in the eastern part of the state. The land is flat. The soil is very rich. Many farms and ranches are here. The Drift Prairie is in the middle of the state. Here the land has hills and valleys cut by rivers. Glaciers moved across this part of the land many years ago. The last region is the Great Plains. Most of the land is flat. But some areas have steep hills. The Badlands are located in this part. It is a wide, dry valley with rocks eroded by wind and rain.

Climate

North Dakota has a continental climate. This means that the summers are very hot, and the winters are very cold. Temperatures can change quickly because there are no large water bodies or landforms, like mountains or forests, to slow the temperature changes. Most of the rain comes in the spring and summer during the growing season.

Natural Resources

The state has large amounts of lignite coal and oil. It also mines gravel, sand, and salt. Most of the state has rich soil. That is why farming is so successful. There are no forests, and water sources are small.

Economy

Over 90 percent of the land in North Dakota is farmed or used to raise cattle. Wheat and sunflower seeds are important crops. Cattle and dairy cows are animals on ranches. Mining is also an important source of money for the state. Oil and lignite coal are its biggest minerals. However, the biggest source of money is made in service jobs. Many people work in insurance companies or banks that help farmers.

NORTH DAKOTA – *The Flickertail State*

North, But Central!

Higher Education

Education was important to many pioneers and immigrants. They felt that an education would help their children be successful. These ideas are still important today. Over 98 percent of students in North Dakota finish high school. A large group of these students go to colleges, universities, or technical schools. They might go to the University of North Dakota. It was started in 1883. It offers classes in law, medicine, and engineering. Students who prefer science may go to the North Dakota State School of Science.

Famous People

Theodore Roosevelt was the 26th President of the United States. He rode with a group of people known as the Rough Riders during the Spanish-American War. He owned two large ranches in the Badlands of North Dakota. A national park has been named for him. Another

famous person was Louis L'Amour. He wrote many stories about cowboys living in the West. Roger Maris was born in North Dakota. He was a famous baseball player. He played for the New York Yankees and the St. Louis Cardinals.

North Dakota Today

Most states have problems with pollution and overcrowding. North Dakota has a very different problem. Many of the students who finish school are leaving the state. They are looking for high-tech jobs that pay a lot of money. Few of these young people want to be farmers or ranchers. Moreover, without a large group of educated people, high-tech companies will not want to build in North Dakota. The people of the state have faced harder problems. They will solve this problem just as they have solved others.

Assessment

Circle the letter of the correct answer.

1. North Dakota is in the center of the _____.
   a. United States
   b. Southwest states
   c. North American continent
   d. world

2. Trappers and traders in the area hunted for _____.
   a. beavers
   b. buffalo
   c. gold
   d. good land

3. The _____ gave people 160 acres if they lived on the land and farmed it for five years.
   a. Wild West Law
   b. Louisiana Purchase
   c. Golden Rule
   d. Homestead Act

4. A continental climate means _____.
   a. temperatures are the same all year long
   b. summers are hot, and winters are cold
   c. summers are cool, and winters are warm
   d. summers are dry, and winters are rainy

5. The most important crop in North Dakota is _____.
   a. wheat
   b. cattle
   c. corn
   d. oil

6. _____ owned two ranches in North Dakota.
   a. Teddy Roosevelt
   b. Roger Maris
   c. Louis L'Amour
   d. Dakota Dan

NORTH DAKOTA – *The Flickertail State*

Name _____ Date _____

Travel Time!

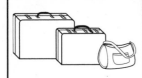

Pack Your Bags!

You will need:
- a road map
- resource books

On the Road!

Here is a list of places to visit in North Dakota. Research to find what each is famous for. Then find each place on a map.
- Badlands
- Bonanzaville USA
- Dakota Dinosaur Museum
- Fort Abraham Lincoln
- Garrison Dam
- International Peace Garden
- National Buffalo Museum
- Theodore Roosevelt National Memorial Park
- Turtle Mountain Indian Reservation
- Whitestone Battlefield Historic Park
- Writing Rock

Snapshots!

Which place would you like to visit? Tell why.

_____

_____

_____

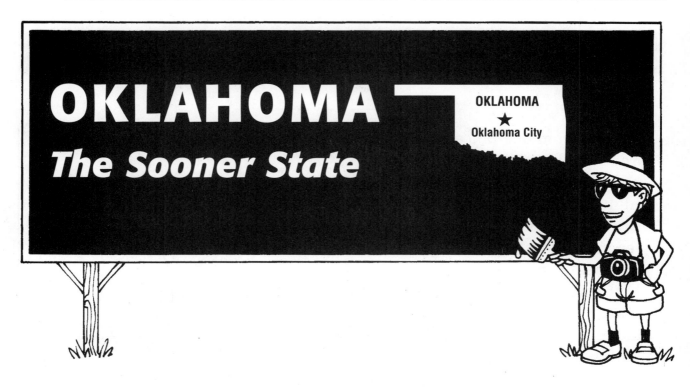

State Your Facts!

Capital: Oklahoma City

Abbreviation: OK

Statehood: November 16, 1907—
the 46th state

Motto: *Labor Omnia Vincit*
("Labor Conquers All")

Bird: Scissortailed flycatcher

Flower: Mistletoe

Tree: Redbud

Area: 69,919 sq mi (181,089 sq
km)—18th in size

Five largest cities: Oklahoma City,
Tulsa, Lawton, Norman, Broken Arrow

Highest point: in western panhandle—
4,973 ft (1,516 m)

Things To Do!

1. A *route* is a way of getting from one place to another. The route map on this page shows highways in the United States. The map key, or legend, shows the different kinds of highways. It also shows state capitals and major cities. Plan a trip from Oklahoma City to Seattle. Try to find out how far that is. Make a list of the highways you would need to use to get

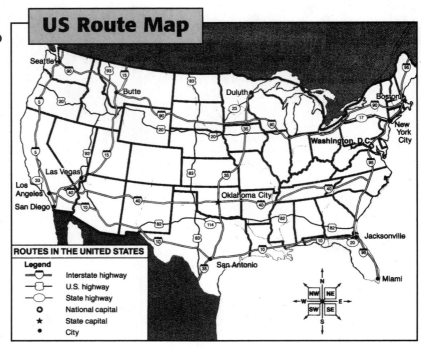

from Oklahoma City to Seattle. Then plan a different route from Seattle to Oklahoma City. How long would such a drive take? Would you camp out or stay in hotels? How much do you think such a trip would cost?

2. Pretend that you are a member of an American Indian group. Your group is being forced to move to Indian Territory. Write a speech that tells your group why they should or should not make the move.

3. Pretend that you are a settler taking part in the Oklahoma Land Rush. It is the morning of April 22, 1889. The shot is about to be fired that will start the rush. How do you feel? Do you think you will get a good piece of land? Write a short essay that tells your feelings. Draw a picture to go with your essay.

4. The Oklahoma state song is "Oklahoma." Learn the song and sing it for your class.

5. Choose one of the famous people from Oklahoma. Write a short biography of that person. Try to find a picture to go with your biography.

It's OK in Oklahoma!

Oklahoma has a long history. It played a key role in the Westward Movement. It was at the heart of the Dust Bowl. It was the site of a terrible bombing in 1995. Things are back to normal now. Read on to see why everything is "OK" in Oklahoma.

History

People have lived in the Oklahoma area for thousands of years. The Paleo-Indians lived there first. About 1,500 years ago, Mound Builders moved into the area. They built huge mounds for their homes and religious sites. Around 500 years ago, other American Indian groups arrived. These included the Pawnee, Cheyenne, and Kiowa. They lived in the eastern and central parts of the area. They followed the buffalo herds across the Great Plains. The Wichita and Caddo groups lived in

the eastern part of the area. They farmed and fished for food.

Spanish explorers arrived in the 1540s. Coronado came first. He was searching for gold in the Seven Cities of Cíbola. He did not find any gold. De Soto came a few years later. He too was seeking gold that he did not find. Both men claimed the Oklahoma area for Spain.

The Spanish did not build settlements in the area. But they did leave one thing that changed the West forever. They brought horses to the New World. Many of the Indian groups learned to ride the horses. The Cheyenne became a powerful group. Cheyenne warriors drove other groups from the area. Some groups, such as the Osage, used the horses to follow the buffalo herds. They gave up their farming lifestyle and became nomadic.

French explorers also visited the area. In the 1680s, La Salle explored the Mississippi River. He claimed all land west of the river for France. Spain and France fought wars over the land. In 1800, Spain gave all its rights to the land to France. In 1803,

OKLAHOMA – *The Sooner State*

It's OK in Oklahoma!

France sold the Oklahoma area to the United States. The area was part of the Louisiana Purchase.

In the 1830s, Oklahoma became part of the "Indian Territory." Settlers in the eastern U.S. wanted more land. They wanted the land that American Indian groups had. So, in 1830, Congress passed the Indian Removal Act. This act forced the Indian groups to leave their homeland. They were moved to land in the Oklahoma area.

The Indian groups were forced to march all the way to the Oklahoma area. The journey was hard. Many Indians died along the way. The path they took became known as the "Trail of Tears."

As the western U.S. was settled, the same thing happened. The American Indians were forced to leave their homeland. They were moved to reservations. Many of these reservations were in Indian Territory.

In 1861, the Civil War began. Eleven Southern states had left the Union. These states were known as the Confederacy. Many Indian groups fought for the Confederacy in the war. A

Cherokee named Stand Waite even became a general in the Confederate Army.

The Confederacy lost the war in 1865. The U.S. government decided to punish the Indian groups for helping the Confederacy. Indian Territory was made much smaller. It was only about half of present-day Oklahoma. The Indians could not leave their reservations, even to hunt for food. The lifestyles of many Indian groups were lost forever.

By 1889, over 60 groups lived in Indian Territory. Settlers had claimed land around the territory. There was also some open land in the middle of the territory. Settlers wanted that land, too. Some settlers entered the territory to claim that land. These people were known as "Sooners." They were turned back by the U.S. Army.

The U.S. government knew it had to do something. In 1889, Congress bought three million acres from the Creek and Seminole groups. This land was

It's OK in Oklahoma!

added to the open land. Then all the land was divided into parcels. The land was then ready to be claimed by settlers.

On the morning of April 22, 1889, over 50,000 homesteaders lined up. They waited on the border of the open land. A shot was fired, and the Oklahoma Land Rush was on. Settlers hurried to stake their claim. By nightfall, two settlements of 10,000 people each had been created!

The eastern half of the Oklahoma area was Indian Territory. The western half was the Oklahoma Territory. In 1907, the two territories joined to become a state. Oklahoma became the 46th state.

Farming was not very good in the state. But the land did contain a valuable product—oil! Many people soon became rich in the oil industry. In World War I, the demand for oil was great. The Oklahoma economy was booming.

But the demand for oil dropped after the war. In the late 1920s, oil prices fell. Prices for farm goods fell, too. In the early 1930s, the Great Depression hit Oklahoma. Banks and businesses failed. People lost their jobs. In 1933, a drought gripped the Great Plains. Rain did not fall for a long time. Crops died, and the soil dried up. Wind whipped up huge clouds of dust. The whole area became known as the "Dust Bowl." Thousands of farmers were forced to leave the state. Many went to California to find a better life.

Finally, the drought ended. Trees and new crops were planted to hold the soil in place. The economy slowly improved. In the 1960s, factories in the state began to make plastics and electronics. The oil and natural gas industry grew. But in the 1980s, the economy stumbled again as prices fell. Now the state works hard to attract new industries.

In 1995, tragedy struck the state. The Murrah Federal Building in Oklahoma City was bombed. Many people were killed.

OKLAHOMA – *The Sooner State*

It's OK in Oklahoma!

Many others worked to rescue survivors and offer help.

Oklahoma people pulled together to help in that tragedy. They will work together to solve the problems of the 21st century. Their motto, "labor conquers all," will see them through the coming years.

Landscape

Oklahoma is a medium-sized state. It measures 230 miles (370 km) from north to south. It is about 464 miles (747 km) wide at its widest point. The state's shape looks like a pan. Its western part is called a "panhandle."

The landscape slopes from its high point in the western part of the state. The low point is in the southeast part. The eastern part has many hills and small mountains. The western section is a part of the High Plains. Major rivers are the Red River, Arkansas River, and Canadian River. There are also many man-made lakes in the state.

Climate

Oklahoma has a fairly mild climate. The average January temperature is about 40° F. The average July temperature is about 83° F. Rainfall ranges from 50 inches in the southeast to 15 inches in the far west.

Natural Resources

Oklahoma has large deposits of oil and natural gas. Coal, zinc, and gypsum are mined there. So are crushed stone, sand, and gravel. Hydroelectric power is made on some of the rivers.

Economy

Oklahoma has a productive economy. Most people there have service jobs. Many work in wholesale and retail trade. Others work in government or social services. Many help tourists who visit the state.

Mining and oil production are important jobs. Oklahoma pumps much oil. Coal, iodine, and limestone are mined there. Manufacturing provides many jobs, too. Some factories make

OKLAHOMA – The Sooner State

It's OK in Oklahoma!

transportation equipment. Others process food products.

Farming is still important in the state. Many farmers raise livestock, such as cattle or chickens. Wheat is the main field crop. Some farms grow peaches, pecans, soybeans, and corn.

Higher Education

Oklahoma has many fine schools. The University of Oklahoma was formed in 1890. Its main campus is in Norman. Oklahoma State University was also created in 1890. Its home campus is in Stillwater.

Famous People

Many famous people have come from Oklahoma. The country humorist Will Rogers was from the state. So was the famous folksinger Woody Guthrie. Maybe you know Guthrie's song "This Land Is Your Land." Jim Thorpe, the legendary athlete, was from Oklahoma. So were baseball player Mickey Mantle and football quarterback Troy Aikman.

Oklahoma Today

Oklahoma's economy is still growing. Now new processing plants are being built. They will process the state's raw materials. Most people now live in cities. The state is looking for new ways to improve in the future. Things will be OK in Oklahoma.

OKLAHOMA – The Sooner State

Assessment

Circle the letter of the correct answer.

1. Spanish explorer Coronado was seeking the _____.
   - **a.** end of the rainbow
   - **b.** Lost City of the Incas
   - **c.** Fountain of Youth
   - **d.** Seven Cities of Cíbola

2. Many American Indian groups were forced to move to _____.
   - **a.** Washington, D.C.
   - **b.** Indian Territory
   - **c.** Oregon Territory
   - **d.** Indiana

3. In 1889, many settlers hurried to claim land in the _____.
   - **a.** Oklahoma Land Rush
   - **b.** California Gold Rush
   - **c.** Louisiana Purchase
   - **d.** Dust Bowl

4. A drought in the 1930s caused Oklahoma to become part of the _____.
   - **a.** Super Bowl
   - **b.** Indian Territory
   - **c.** Dust Bowl
   - **d.** Great Depression

Number the events in the order they happened.

_____ The Oklahoma Land Rush took place.

_____ La Salle claimed the Oklahoma area for France.

_____ The Civil War began in 1861.

_____ Oklahoma became the 46th state.

_____ The Murrah Federal Building in Oklahoma City was bombed.

_____ Mound Builders lived in the Oklahoma area.

OKLAHOMA – *The Sooner State*

Travel Time!

Oklahoma offers many kinds of vacation fun. If you like history, there are many places to visit. Start in Oklahoma City. It's in the center of the state. There you can see oil wells on the Capitol lawn. You can also visit the National Cowboy Hall of Fame and Western Heritage Center. This is a group of museums. One museum honors people who worked hard on the open range. Another museum is about Western movie actors, such as John Wayne. Another features Western artists, such as Charles Russell and Fredric Remington. The Rodeo Hall of Fame is there, too.

Just north of Oklahoma City is Guthrie. It was one of the towns created during the Oklahoma Land Rush in 1889. Much of the town remains as it was in those times. In north-central Oklahoma is Ponca City. There you can see the Pioneer Woman Statue. It honors the proud pioneer women who helped to settle the frontier.

In northeast Oklahoma is Muskogee. There you can tour Fort Gibson Military Park. It dates back to the days of Indian Territory. Muskogee also has the Five Civilized Tribes Museum. It features the art and culture of several American Indian groups.

For outdoor fun, try Ouachita National Forest. It's near Heavener, in east-central Oklahoma. You can camp or boat there. You can also hike in the Ouachita Mountains. Also try the Chickasaw National Recreation Area. It's near Sulphur, in south-central Oklahoma. There you can camp and hike. There are many springs in the area. You can also have fun in the water there in the Lake of the Arbuckles. For a good fishing trip, try Lake Texoma. It is on the border with Texas, near Durant.

Another fun place is Alabaster Caverns State Park. It's near Camp Houston, in north Oklahoma. It features one of the largest gypsum caves in the world. Whatever you choose, your vacation time in Oklahoma will be OK.

Name _____ Date _____

Travel Time!

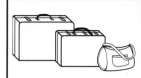

Pack Your Bags!

- Find a road map of Oklahoma. Then draw your own map of the state. Show the major highways on your map. Which roads would you use to go from your home to Stillwater? Color those roads blue. Which roads would you use to go from your home to the state capital? Color those roads red. What is the state capital of Oklahoma?
- Find a map of Oklahoma. Find 20 cities or towns in the state. Then write the names of those places in ABC order.

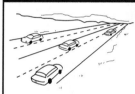

On the Road!

- Which of the places on your list would you like to visit? Why? Write a short paper telling your reasons. How far is the place from your home? How much do you think a bus ticket to go there would cost? How much do you think a one-week trip there would cost altogether?

Snapshots!

- Draw a picture of yourself as a rodeo rider.
- Write a poem about being a pioneer. Draw a picture to go with your poem.
- Pretend you are driving in the Midget Car Race. Write a short story or poem about the race. Do you win? Include a picture.
- Draw a picture of you and your family fishing on Lake Texoma.

OKLAHOMA – *The Sooner State*

Name ______________________________ Date ____________________

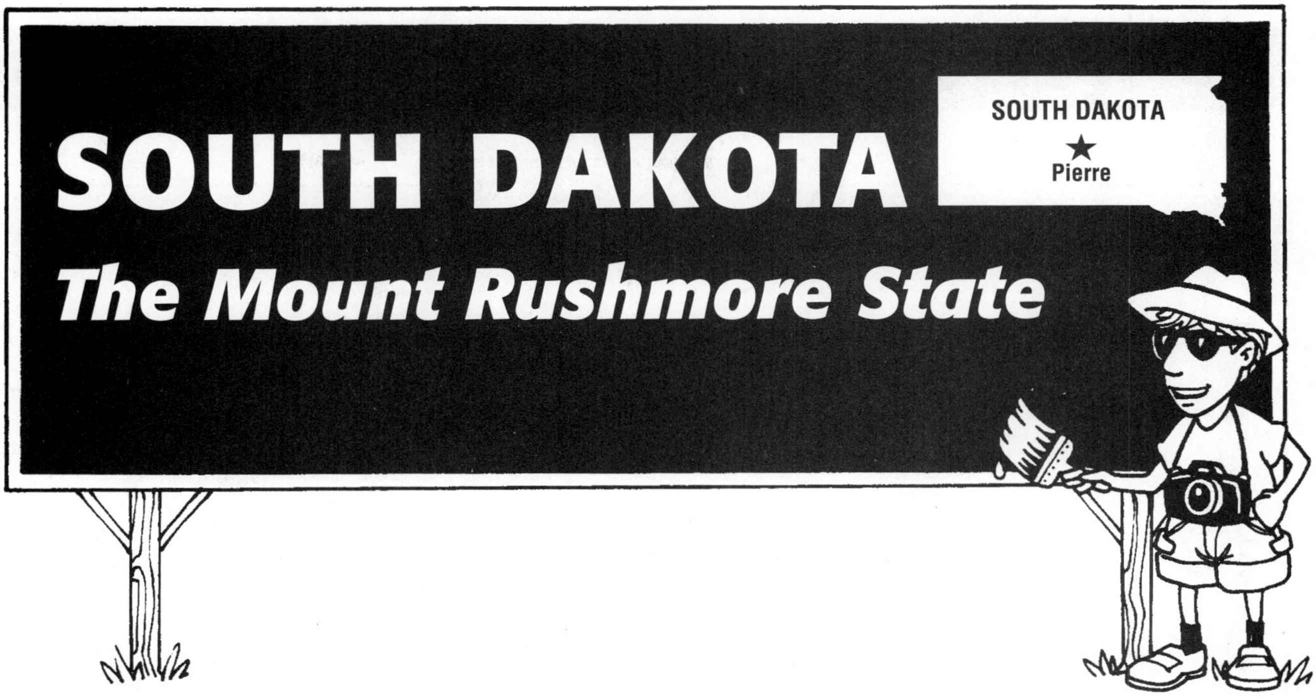
SOUTH DAKOTA
The Mount Rushmore State
SOUTH DAKOTA
Pierre

State Your Facts!

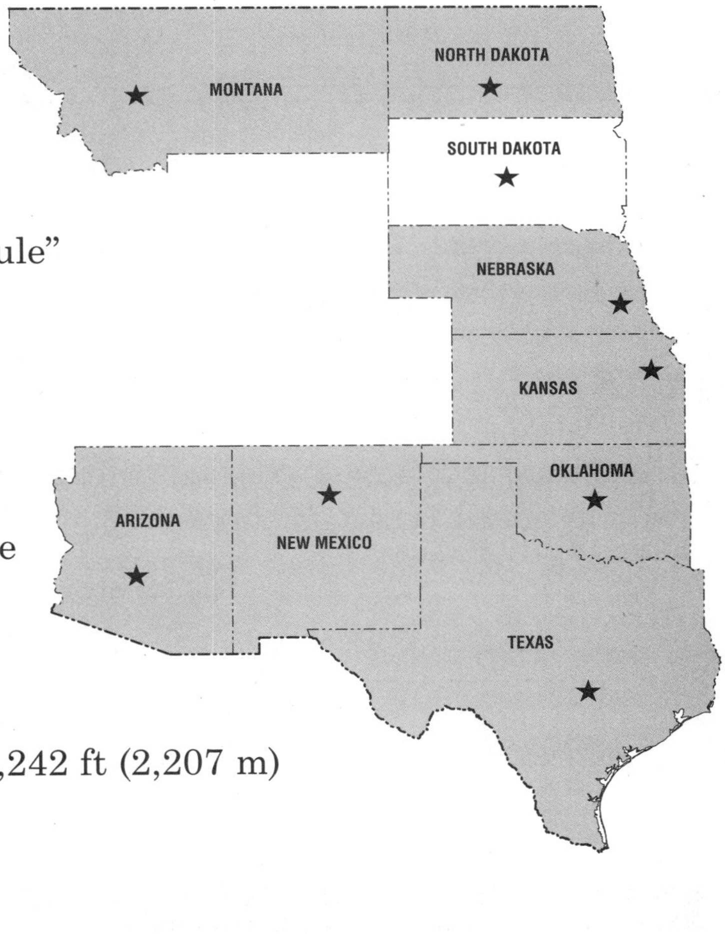
MONTANA
NORTH DAKOTA
SOUTH DAKOTA
NEBRASKA
KANSAS
OKLAHOMA
ARIZONA
NEW MEXICO
TEXAS

Capital: Pierre

Abbreviation: SD

Statehood: November 2, 1889—
the 40th state

Motto: "Under God the People Rule"

Bird: Ring-necked pheasant

Flower: American pasqueflower

Tree: Black Hills spruce

Area: 77,122 sq mi
(199,744 sq km)—16th in size

Five largest cities: Sioux Falls, Rapid City, Aberdeen, Watertown, Brookings

Highest point: Harney Peak—7,242 ft (2,207 m)

Name _____ Date _____

Things To Do!

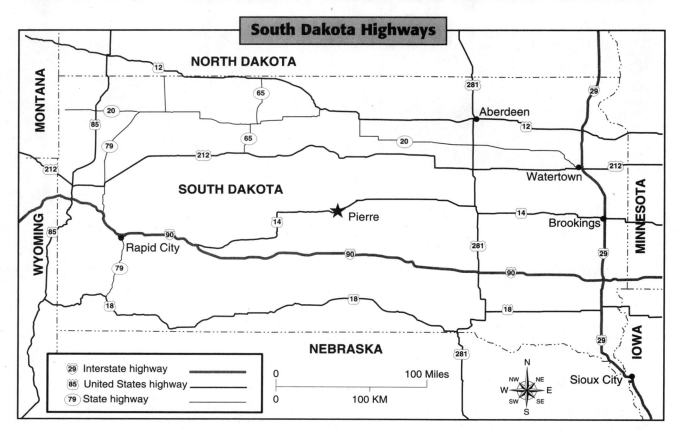

South Dakota Highways

A. List the states that border South Dakota.

1. _____ 4. _____

2. _____ 5. _____

3. _____ 6. _____

B. Use the road map to chart a nonstop trip to visit each state along South Dakota's border.

_____

_____

_____

_____

See South Dakota!

The state seal of South Dakota looks like a sun on the outside. The inside of the seal shows a furnace, a riverboat on a river, cattle grazing, and a farmer plowing a field. How are these pictures part of South Dakota? Come see!

History

A native tribe called the Arikara lived around the Missouri River in the area now called South Dakota. They grew corn and hunted buffalo for food and clothing. The Cheyenne and Sioux, other Native American groups, began moving to the land in the 1700s. They were pushed off their hunting grounds in the East by the growing number of settlers looking for new land. They lived in teepees and followed the buffalo.

The French were the first Europeans to claim the land in 1682. However, people did not travel to the region for another hundred years. In 1803, the United States bought the land from France. The famous American explorers Meriwether Lewis and William Clark spent seven weeks in the South Dakota area. They wrote about the rich land. Fur trappers and traders quickly came to the area.

The first settlement was built in 1859. The Dakota Territory was formed in 1861. The territory included North Dakota, South Dakota, and parts of Montana and Wyoming. Settlers began to move to the area to set up farms and ranches along the rivers. Crops could be moved along the rivers easily. At first, the Native Americans, settlers, and trappers lived together peacefully. However, as more people came to the land, the native tribes became angry.

In the 1860s, Montana and Wyoming formed two new territories. Gold was discovered in Montana Territory, and people flooded into the area. To make travel easier, the United States began building a road, called the Bozeman Trail, through Dakota Territory. The road was in the middle of the Sioux hunting ground. The Native Americans, led by Chief Red Cloud, attacked the workers. The army was sent to protect the workers. By 1868, the government stopped building the trail because of continued fighting. The land west of the Missouri River in present-day South Dakota was given to the Sioux.

SOUTH DAKOTA – *The Mount Rushmore State*

See South Dakota!

The army then began to keep settlers away from the Sioux land. People traveled into the area anyway. In 1875, gold was discovered in the Black Hills, a mountain area in the western part of the region. The gold rush was on in present-day South Dakota. Several Sioux tribes joined together to try to stop the people from entering their land. More troops were sent to Dakota Territory. By 1877, the fighting was over. The Sioux were told to leave the Black Hills.

There were enough people in Dakota Territory to form two states. In 1889, the land was divided in half to form the states of North Dakota and South Dakota.

In 1890, the Sioux began Ghost Dances. They believed the dances would scare away the settlers and help the buffalo come back. More Native Americans joined the dances. The United States government told the group to stop. Once again the army and the Native Americans began to fight. One native group was forced to camp at Wounded Knee. As soldiers gathered the weapons from the Native Americans, a gun fired. The army then fired on the Native

Americans, killing them all. It was the last big Native American battle. The Sioux were moved to reservations.

Settlers quickly moved into the area. They farmed the land and raised cattle. The people did well until 1911. There was little rain for several years. The state was in a drought. Farmers left the land to look for other jobs.

The whole nation ran into trouble in the 1930s. Banks and businesses closed. People were out of work. The government found jobs for many people. In South Dakota, workers built roads and parks in the Black Hills. Farmers were given new kinds of grain that would not need as much water. When World War II started in 1941, South Dakota was back to work.

Over the last half of the century, there have been problems between the Native Americans and the government. A dam caused flooding to farmland on a reservation. Another time, Native Americans felt that the government did not listen to them. Some Native Americans took over Wounded Knee, the site of the last Native

American battle, for several months. In 1980, the United States Supreme Court said the government must pay for the Black Hills land taken from the Sioux. The Sioux wanted part of the land instead. The problem has not yet been solved.

Landscape

South Dakota has four main land regions. Glaciers, large sheets of ice, moved across the eastern part of the state many years ago. They shaped the land in most of the state. The glaciers left behind clay, sand, and gravel. The Drift Prairie has rolling hills. Most of the state's lakes are here. The Dissected Till Plains are in the southeastern region. The Great Plains cover most of South Dakota. In this part are plains, hills, and canyons. Steep hills, called buttes, rise up in the grassy plains. The Badlands are in the Great Plains. The land has wide, dry valleys where wind and rain have eroded the rocky hills. The last area is the Black Hills. It is a small mountain group in the western part of the state.

Climate

Summers in South Dakota are very hot. Temperatures in some areas can reach 110° F. Winters are very cold, with temperatures often dropping below zero. This kind of climate is a continental climate. Since there are no large water bodies, mountains, or forests, temperatures change quickly.

Natural Resources

The state has a variety of natural resources. Gold is an important mineral. The Black Hills have mines that have more gold than any other place in the Western Hemisphere. Petroleum, sand, and gravel are also mined.

Economy

Most people in South Dakota work in service jobs. They help other people who shop in stores. They also work in banks, insurance companies, and tourist services. However, the state leads the nation in growing hay and rye, a grain. Ranchers raise cattle and sheep. For manufacturing, people in South Dakota have jobs that make

SOUTH DAKOTA – *The Mount Rushmore State*

See South Dakota!

products from the crops or animals farmers raise. The state also manufactures electronic goods, like computers.

Higher Education

There are several well-known colleges and universities in South Dakota. The South Dakota School of Mines and Technology opened in 1885 when South Dakota was still part of Dakota Territory. Mining was important to the territory, and the school taught people about minerals, mining, and making the minerals into other goods. The college is now a leading school in science and technology. Sinte Gleska College was the first Native American college in the nation. It started in 1969. It began because people on a reservation thought that the children were forgetting the language and culture of the Lakota, a group that is part of the Sioux nation. The school's name is the Lakota name for the Indian brave Spotted Tail.

Famous People

Crazy Horse was a Native American. He was a member of the Sioux nation. He led his people against United States soldiers to keep gold miners and settlers out of the Black Hills. Laura Ingalls Wilder wrote books about living on the prairie. The books tell the stories about growing up on the South Dakota prairie. Her most famous book is *Little House on the Prairie*. Tom Brokaw is also from South Dakota. He is on television. He tells what is happening in the world on the news each weeknight.

South Dakota Today

South Dakota is a young state. Overcrowding and pollution are not a problem as in other states. The problem facing the state is different. The state needs to find a way to get more companies to come to the state. Young people who finish college and high school are leaving to get better jobs in other states. Also, many reservations are in South Dakota. Many people on these reservations are poor. Health care and education are big concerns. There are even fewer jobs available on reservations. However, the Native Americans are working to remember their customs and language. Working together, the people of the state should be able to solve the problems as they move into the new century.

SOUTH DAKOTA – *The Mount Rushmore State*

Assessment

Circle the letter of the correct answer.

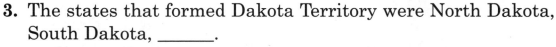

1. The _____ lived in teepees and followed the buffalo.
   - **a.** French
   - **b.** Sioux
   - **c.** English
   - **d.** Arikara

2. The workers stopped building the Bozeman Trail because _____.
   - **a.** they wanted to mine gold instead
   - **b.** the money ran out
   - **c.** the soldiers took over the road
   - **d.** the Sioux kept attacking the workers

3. The states that formed Dakota Territory were North Dakota, South Dakota, _____.
   - **a.** Minnesota, and Wyoming
   - **b.** Montana, and Wyoming
   - **c.** Minnesota, and Nebraska
   - **d.** Nebraska, and Montana

4. The last big battle between Native Americans and the United States government took place at _____.
   - **a.** Pierre
   - **b.** Sioux Falls
   - **c.** the Bozeman Trail
   - **d.** Wounded Knee

5. The most important mineral South Dakota mines is _____.
   - **a.** gold
   - **b.** sand
   - **c.** oil
   - **d.** hay

6. _____ wrote stories about growing up on the prairie of South Dakota.
   - **a.** Tom Brokaw
   - **b.** Chief Red Cloud
   - **c.** Laura Ingalls Wilder
   - **d.** Meriwether Lewis

SOUTH DAKOTA – *The Mount Rushmore State*

Travel Time!

Pack Your Bags!

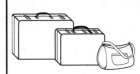

You will need:
- a United States road map

Mount Rushmore is a big mountain in which the heads of Presidents George Washington, Thomas Jefferson, Theodore Roosevelt, and Abraham Lincoln are carved. Each head is about as tall as a six-story building. The Crazy Horse Memorial is another sculpture that is being carved in a mountain. It is just 17 miles away from Mount Rushmore. When done, it will show the great Native American warrior Crazy Horse sitting on his horse. It will be the biggest sculpture in the world when it is finished.

On the Road!

- You want to visit Mount Rushmore and the Crazy Horse Memorial. Make a plan to get there on another sheet of paper.
- Use the road map to plan the route you will take to get there from your home.
- If you drive an average speed of 60 miles per hour for seven hours each day, how long will it take you?

Snapshots!

- Each President's head at Mount Rushmore is about 60 feet tall. The head of Crazy Horse will be about 90 feet tall when it is done. Draw a picture to scale that shows you in front of one of the heads.

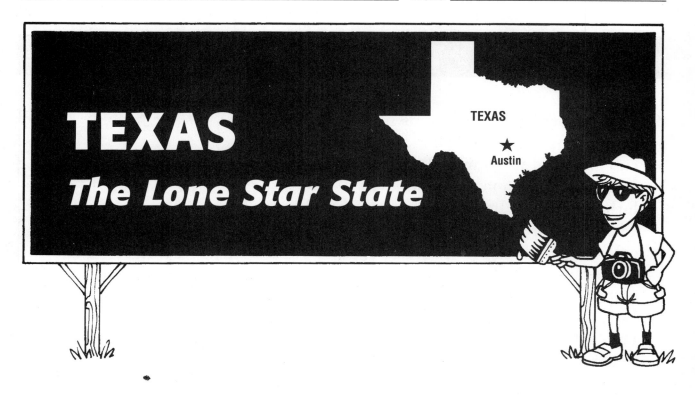

State Your Facts!

Capital: Austin

Abbreviation: TX

Statehood: December 29, 1845— the 28th state

Motto: "Friendship"

Bird: Mockingbird

Flower: Bluebonnet

Tree: Pecan

Area: 266,874 sq mi (691,201 sq km)—2nd in size

Five largest cities: Houston, San Antonio, Dallas, El Paso, Austin

Highest point: Guadalupe Peak—8,751 ft (2,667 m)

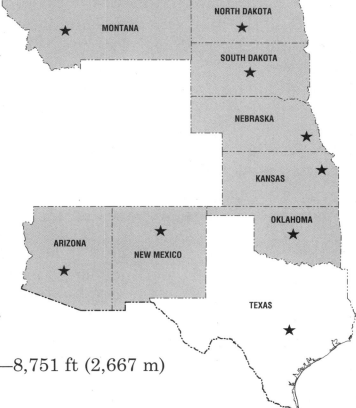

Things To Do!

1. Most globes and world maps have a grid of lines on them. The lines that run east and west are called *lines of latitude*. The Equator is a line of latitude. It is called 0° (zero degrees). The area north of the Equator is called the Northern Hemisphere. The area south of the Equator is called the Southern Hemisphere.

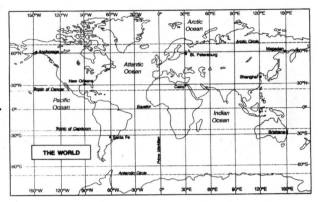

Lines of latitude north of the Equator are marked with an *N*. The North Pole is 90° N. Lines south of the Equator are marked with an *S*. The South Pole is 90° S.

   The lines that run north and south are called *lines of longitude*. The Prime Meridian is a line of longitude. It is in Great Britain. The area east of this line is called the Eastern Hemisphere. To the west of this line is the Western Hemisphere. Lines of longitude east of this line are marked with an *E*. Lines to the west of this line are marked with a *W*.

   Find the lines of latitude and longitude near your town. Use the lines to estimate your town's location. When you write latitude and longitude, you write the line of latitude first. For example, the latitude and longitude for Austin, Texas, is about 30° N, 98° W. Write the latitude and longitude of your town.

2. Now follow the line of latitude near your town east or west. Find a big city somewhere in the world that is near that line. Write the name of the city. Now follow the line of longitude near your town north or south. Find a city somewhere in the world near that line. Write the name of the city.

3. Get your teacher or an adult to help you with this activity. Write down the latitude and longtitude for your town. Then go on the Internet. Go to this address: **http://www.fourmilab.ch/cgi-bin/uncgi/Earth**

   This is the web address for EarthCam. At this site you can type in your latitude and longitude. Then you can see your area from a camera in space!

TEXAS – *The Lone Star State*

It's Time for Texas!

Texas has an unusual history. It is the only state that was first a country. People in Texas stand alone. That is what the lone star on the Texas flag means. But they are also friendly.

History

Europeans first arrived in the Texas area in the early 1500s. At that time, several American Indian groups lived there. The largest group was the Caddo people. They lived in the Red River valley. They were good farmers. They also made pottery, cloth, and baskets.

Spanish explorers arrived in the 1520s. Cabeza de Vaca was the first. He and his men shipwrecked on the Texas coast. They had come looking for gold. Other Spanish explorers followed, all seeking gold. They did not find any gold.

In 1682, Spanish Catholic missionaries built Ysleta. It was the first European settlement in Texas. In 1685, the French explorer La Salle built a colony on the Texas coast. He named it Fort Saint Louis. But La Salle was killed by one of his men. Local Indians killed the other Frenchmen and burned the fort.

Over the next 100 years, more missions and towns were built in the Texas area. But by 1793, only about 7,000 European settlers lived there. In 1819, Moses Austin visited the town of San Antonio. He won a grant from Spain to bring American settlers into Texas. But in 1821, Mexico won its independence from Spain. Texas became part of Mexico. Soon after that, Moses Austin died.

His son, Stephen F. Austin, received his father's grant. About 300 families were allowed to settle on 200,000 acres in Texas. The settlers began to arrive in 1823. Austin's grant was located along the lower Brazos and Colorado rivers. Other people also won grants to bring settlers into Texas.

Trouble soon started between the settlers and Mexico. The settlers felt more ties to the United States than to Mexico. They wanted Texas to become part of the U.S. The settlers also wanted representatives in the Mexican government. Stephen Austin went to Mexico City in 1833. He gave a

TEXAS – *The Lone Star State*

It's Time for Texas!

list of complaints to the Mexican government. It granted only a few of his wishes. On the way back to Texas, Austin was arrested by the Mexicans. He had written a letter saying that Texas should start its own government. Austin was released from jail after several months.

A war between the settlers and Mexico began in 1835. It was called the Texas Revolution. The Mexican army was led by General Santa Anna. The Texans quickly drove the Mexican soldiers from Gonzales. Then Texans led by Stephen Austin captured San Antonio. A temporary government was set up. Sam Houston was named leader of the Texas troops.

On March 2, 1836, Texas declared its independence from Mexico. On March 6, after 13 days of fighting, the Mexican army captured the Alamo. The Alamo was an old Spanish mission. During the fight, 183 volunteers died for Texas independence. They were led by William Travis, Jim Bowie, and David Crockett. Several days later, over 300 Texans were

captured near the San Antonio River. They were marched to Goliad. There, under the order of General Santa Anna, the Texans were killed.

Meanwhile, Sam Houston and his troops retreated toward what is now Houston. The Mexican army followed. On April 21, 1836, Houston and his troops were near the San Jacinto River. Santa Anna's army was nearby. As the Mexicans slept during their siesta, the Texans attacked. Their battle cries were "Remember the Alamo! Remember Goliad!" The Battle of San Jacinto was over in only a few minutes. The Texans had won. Santa Anna was captured. He signed a treaty that gave Texas its independence. Then he left Texas with his army.

Texas then became a separate country. Sam Houston was elected as the first President of the Republic of Texas. Texas at the time was a wild, lawless place. The Texas Rangers were formed to keep peace on the Texas frontier. This group of law officers is still active today. In 1845, the United States agreed to annex Texas. Texas became the 28th state.

When the Civil War came, Texas seceded, or left the Union.

It's Time for Texas!

Texas soldiers fought for the Confederacy. Civil War battles in Texas were mostly on the coast. Major battles were at Galveston, Sabine Pass, and the Red River. The last battle of the war took place near Brownsville. It happened in May 1865. That was a month after the Confederacy had surrendered! News of the surrender had not yet reached Texas.

After the Civil War, many Texans turned to cattle ranching. Cowboys went on cattle drives along the Chisholm Trail and other famous routes. The large herds were moved to the railroad centers in Kansas and Missouri. By 1900, though, the railroads had reached Texas. The days of the great cattle drives were over.

In 1901, oil was discovered in east Texas. The oil field was called Spindletop. Soon oil was found in many places in Texas. Oil became the "black gold" of the Texas economy. Texas was struck by the Great Depression in the 1930s. But the oil industry continued to do well. The drought that dried up the Great Plains in the 1930s also hit Texas. Much farmland was ruined. Sections of Texas became part of the Dust Bowl.

Two very important things happened in Texas in the 1960s. In 1963, President John Kennedy was shot and killed in Dallas. The whole nation mourned his death. Also in the early 1960s, the National Aeronautics and Space Administration (NASA) built a space center near Houston. In 1969, NASA put the first astronaut on the Moon.

In the 1980s, Texans began to elect women to many important offices. Most of the major cities had a woman mayor. In 1990, Ann Richards was elected governor. Later in the 1990s, Texas became an important high-tech center. Many computer and software companies opened in Austin and Houston.

Texas now has problems with pollution, poverty, and crime. But Texas people are taking big steps to solve these problems.

Landscape

Texas is the second largest state. It measures 737 miles (1,186 km) from north to south. It is about 774 miles (1,245 km) wide. It has 367 miles (591 km) of coastline on the Gulf of Mexico.

TEXAS – The Lone Star State

It's Time for Texas!

Texas is broken into five sections. In the east are the Piney Woods. Here are many forests, lakes, and the Big Thicket. In the southeast part are the Gulf Coastal Plains. This area is mostly level and grassy. It reaches 50 to 100 miles inland. In central Texas is the Hill Country. This is an area of hills and rolling land. In north and northwest Texas are plains. This is the southern edge of the Great Plains. Finally, in the west are mountains and mesas. This is a dry area, with many mountains and desert places.

There are several major rivers in Texas. These include the Rio Grande, Red, Pecos, Colorado, and Brazos rivers. There are many natural and man-made lakes in the state. There are also bays along the coast that serve as harbors. Houston is also a major port city. But it is connected to the gulf by the man-made Houston Ship Channel.

Climate

Because Texas is so large, it has a varied climate. Places along the coast can be windy, hot, and humid. Places in the west can be very hot and dry. Places in the Panhandle can be below 0° F in the winter. In general, Texas has mild winters and hot summers. Rainfall ranges from 50 inches a year in the east to under 10 inches in the west. Very little snow falls in most of the state. The Panhandle section receives about 20 inches of snow a year.

Natural Resources

Texas has large deposits of oil and natural gas. Sulphur, limestone, sand, and gravel are mined in the state. So are clay, magnesium, and some coal. The eastern section of Texas has many forests that are used for logging. The waters of the Gulf of Mexico provide seafood. The soil of Texas is another resource. Farming is important in many parts of the state.

Economy

The Texas economy has many pieces. In the east half of the state, there are many kinds of jobs. People work on cotton or rice farms. They work in logging in the eastern forests. They fish in the waters of the gulf. They work in the many oil refineries and chemical plants in

TEXAS – The Lone Star State

It's Time for Texas!

the coastal area. They work in factories. Computers, electronics, medicines, and other things are made there. In the west part, many people work in mining or ranching. There are also several vineyards in central and west Texas.

Most people in Texas, though, have service jobs. They work in health, business, or retail services. Many also work to help the many tourists that visit Texas each year.

Higher Education

Texas has many fine colleges and universities. Two major schools are Texas A & M University and the University of Texas. Texas A & M began in 1876. Its main campus is in College Station. The University of Texas started in 1883. It is centered in Austin. Rice University in Houston is another important school. It was created in 1891.

Famous People

Many famous people have come from Texas. The 34th U.S. President, Dwight Eisenhower, was born in Denison. The 36th President, Lyndon Johnson, was born and lived in the state. The 41st President, George Bush, also

lives in the state. Barbara Jordan was an important African-American legislator from Texas.

Texas has produced many famous people in entertainment. Writers J. Frank Dobie and Larry McMurtry lived there. Country singers Willie Nelson, George Strait, Tanya Tucker, and Leann Rimes are from Texas. The famous blues singer Lightnin' Hopkins and Tejano star Selena were also from the state. Actors Matthew McConaughey, Tommy Lee Jones, Sissy Spacek, and Farrah Fawcett are well-known Texans.

Texas Today

Many people think all of Texas is a wild place. They think all Texans are cowboys. There are still wild places in the state. Many people still wear cowboy hats and boots. But Texas is a modern place, ready to help lead the U.S. into the 21st century.

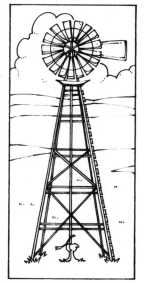

TEXAS – The Lone Star State

Assessment

Circle the letter of the correct answer.

1. The first European settlement in Texas was _____.
   - **a.** Houston
   - **b.** Caddo
   - **c.** Ysleta
   - **d.** Austin

2. Many American settlers were led into Texas by _____.
   - **a.** Daniel Boone
   - **b.** Stephen Austin
   - **c.** Sam Houston
   - **d.** William Travis

3. The leader of the Mexican army in the
   Texas Revolution was _____.
   - **a.** Santa Fe
   - **b.** Santa Claus
   - **c.** San Antonio
   - **d.** Santa Anna

4. One battle cry at the Battle of San Jacinto was _____.
   - **a.** "Remember Gonzales!"
   - **b.** "Remember the Alamo!"
   - **c.** "Remember your guns!"
   - **d.** "How about those Cowboys?"

Number the events in the order they happened.

_____ Oil was discovered at Spindletop.

_____ Spanish explorers visited the Texas area.

_____ Cowboys made cattle drives to Kansas and Missouri.

_____ The Texas Revolution began.

_____ NASA's space center was built near Houston.

_____ Texas became the 28th state in 1845.

Travel Time!

Texas has many different things to see and do. Start along the Gulf Coast. Near Houston, you can tour the Lyndon B. Johnson Space Center. You can see how the astronauts train to go into space. Also near Houston is the San Jacinto Monument. It honors the last battle of the Texas Revolution. Near the monument, you can inspect the restored battleship *Texas*. It was the last of the great battleships called dreadnoughts. Also in Houston is the Astrodome. It was the first domed stadium. Near the Dome is Astroworld, a fun park. Houston is in southeast Texas, 50 miles (80 km) from the coast.

Southeast of Houston is the island city of Galveston. There you can visit Moody Gardens. It features a collection of unusual plants and animals. You can also enjoy the warm waters of the Gulf of Mexico. Galveston has miles of beaches. Just northeast of Galveston, you can travel by ferry to the Bolivar Peninsula. There you can visit the Bolivar Lighthouse.

Southwest of Galveston, there are hundreds of miles of beaches. About 200 miles down the coast is Corpus Christi. There you can visit the Texas State Aquarium. You can also tour the aircraft carrier *Lexington*. Just southeast of Corpus Christi is Padre Island National Seashore. There you can have fun in the surf.

Heading inland, about 150 miles to the northwest, you'll reach San Antonio. There you can stroll along the popular River Walk. You can eat your fill of Tex-Mex food. Be sure to visit the Alamo there, too. About 90 miles to the northeast is Austin. There you can visit the state capital and swim in the many area lakes.

About 200 miles north of Austin is the Dallas-Fort Worth area. There you can have fun at Six Flags over Texas. It offers many rides and attractions. You may also get to see the Cowboys, Rangers, or Mavericks play ball.

Then head west—way west— over 500 miles. Yes, you're still in Texas. You will be in the heart of the mountain and desert section of Texas. Along the border with Mexico is Big Bend National Park.

TEXAS – *The Lone Star State*

There you can hike, camp, or raft along the Rio Grande. The park provides a rugged view of nature. Just north of the park is the Big Bend State Ranch. It is a state park with 250,000 acres of rocky land.

About 100 miles north of these parks is Fort Davis. There you can visit the McDonald Observatory.

Its mountaintop location offers a fabulous view of the stars.

There are places to hike, camp, swim, and boat all over Texas. Whatever you choose, you will have a great time in the Lone Star State.

Pack Your Bags!

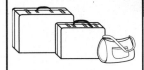

- Plan a one-week camping trip to Big Bend National Park. You will camp out every night. What camping supplies will you need? Don't forget food and water. Make a list of all the supplies you will have to take. Plan a menu for each day. How much do you think your trip will cost?
- Texas has many rivers. Would you like to canoe down one? How far do you think you could canoe in one day? Choose one of the rivers in Texas. Figure out how long the river is. How long would your canoe trip down the river take?

On the Road!

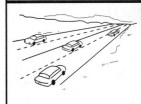

- One fun thing to do while driving is to watch for license plates from other states. How many can you see? How far away are those states?

Snapshots!

- Draw a picture of the Astrodome.